PHENOMENAL
PHYSICS

METRO BOOKS
New York

An Imprint of Sterling Publishing Co., Inc.
1166 Avenue of the Americas
New York, NY 10036

ISBN: 978-1-4351-6250-1

For information about custom editions, special sales, and premium and corporate purchases, please
contact Sterling Special Sales at 800-805-5489 or specialsales@sterlingpublishing.com.

Manufactured in China

2 4 6 8 10 9 7 5 3

www.sterlingpublishing.com

Design by Lindsey Johns

Image credits
• Creative Commons: 65 © Andshel, 89 (bottom left) © Ute Kraus, 110 © GF Hund, 122 © Bengt
  Nyman, 141 (bottom) © Lucas Taylor
• Getty Images: 61 © Hulton Archive, 79 © Time Life Pictures, 111 © Keystone, 124 © Joe Munroe,
  137 © Jim Smeal
• Misc: 14 © Luc Viatour (www.lucnix.be)
• Science Photo Library: 114 © American Institute of Physics, 118 © Lawrence Berkley Laboratory
• Shutterstock: 9, 36, 45 (top right), 48, 49, 73, 82, 89 (bottom right and top), 105
• Wellcome Trust: 57 & 69 (both) © Wellcome Trust. These images come from Wellcome Images, a
  website operated by Wellcome Trust, a global charitable foundation based in the United Kingdom

PHENOMENAL PHYSICS

A TOTALLY NON-SCARY GUIDE TO PHYSICS AND WHY IT MATTERS

Isaac McPhee

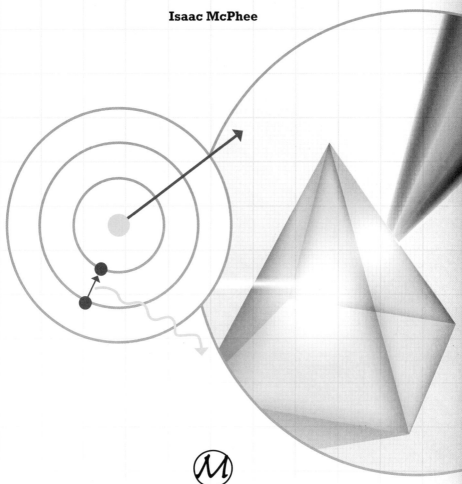

METRO BOOKS

NEW YORK

Contents

Electron orbits: see
Wave–Particle Duality
(pp. 108-109)

"Look deep into nature, and
then you will understand
everything better."

—**Albert Einstein**

What Is Physics?

"Physics" is derived from the Greek word *physis*, which means "nature." Physics explores the mysteries of how nature behaves. The purpose of physics is to ask every question that can be asked about how things work, and then to search for the answers to these questions. There are no clear limits to the scope of physics: it seeks to explain energy and matter, and how they work together; it investigates natural phenomena, from the entire universe down to the tiniest pieces of the atom. The study of physics carries with it a wealth of fascinating mysteries, which is what makes it so exciting.

From Quarks to Quasars

Few fields of study are larger in scope than physics. Within this all-encompassing science lie answers to questions about the nature of the universe itself: its shape, its content, and its history. By applying the same physical principles by which we look at the universe as a whole, we can gaze into the mysteries of the tiniest specks of matter. A physicist can observe the light from distant galaxies known as quasars—the most luminous objects in the known universe—as well as the interaction between quarks, the almost unbelievably small particles within the atomic nucleus.

Physics lies at the root of all other sciences. Everything in the universe, whether or not it can be seen, can be reduced to the most basic physical laws. Every field of study that concerns itself with the material world—from chemistry and biology to astronomy and even engineering—is ultimately nothing more than physics. Chemistry is the study of the chemical elements (atoms), their properties, and how they bond together to form compounds and substances. Biology is the study of living creatures, made up of cells, which are made up of atoms. Engineering is the study of materials, strengths, and forces. All three of these fall within the study of physics.

"To those who do not know mathematics it is difficult to get across a real feeling as to the beauty, the deepest beauty, of nature."

—Richard Feynman

How Physics Is Done

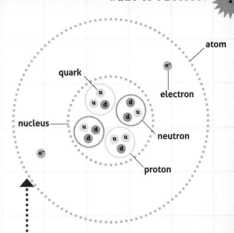

With such a grand scope, how can physicists even begin to answer all the questions posed by the universe? The answer lies in the fact that within physics there are multiple very specific disciplines, and most physicists today have taken up very specialized approaches to their chosen field. These are just a few of the largest disciplines:

Particle physics looks at the smallest things in the universe: atoms and subatomic particles. It is one of the most exciting scientific fields today. Particle physicists use both theory and experiment to explore the mysteries hidden within the tiniest pieces of matter in the universe, seeking to answer questions about the origins of the universe and the basic building blocks of all matter.

The study of physics at a subatomic level has revealed atoms to be made up of even smaller particles, among which are six types of quarks (see p. 131).

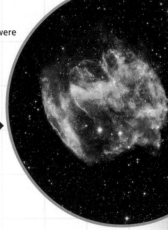

Until supernovas (exploding stars) were discovered, most philosophers believed that the stars were unchanging.

Astrophysics (also known as "high-energy physics") explores the universe, looking at phenomena such as stars, galaxies, black holes, quasars, pulsars, and supernovas. It applies principles such as relativity and quantum mechanics to objects in our solar system and beyond.

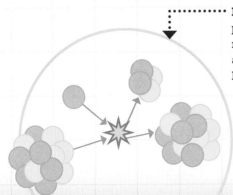

Nuclear physics uncovers the potential hidden within the atomic nucleus, helping to develop newer and more efficient forms of energy. From nuclear physics come nuclear weapons, nuclear power, and numerous advances in medicine, engineering, and even exploring our own history (using radioactive dating techniques).

Within each of these fields, physicists can generally be divided into two broad categories: theorists and experimenters. Theorists seek to utilize the incredible power of very complicated mathematical tools in order to get to the bottom of physical mysteries. They use tried and true methods of calculation in order to take previous experiments and observations and to generalize from them, predicting future developments or finding better explanations for those phenomena which have already been observed.

Experimenters seek to explore the physical universe by putting it to the test. Using equipment as simple as a microscope or as complicated as a multi-billion-dollar particle accelerator, experimenters must be clever, creative, and, above all, precise. They are able to manipulate and observe the smallest bits of matter known to man and observe the farthest reaches of space with unbelievable accuracy, giving us all a more detailed and accurate picture of our universe. Experimental physicists throughout modern history have been on the cutting edge of technology, using the mental and technological tools at their disposal to provide new insights into the workings of nature.

Modern physics explores paradoxical concepts such as antimatter and, shown here, black holes (see pp. 134–5).

Asking Questions

Although physicists deal with the most perplexing concepts in the natural world, they must first learn which questions to ask. Asking the right questions can lead them to expose even greater mysteries, which is where discovery begins. Physicists throughout history have begun by asking the most basic questions and then proceeded to delve deeper into the problems that are uncovered.

We can ask, as Isaac Newton did, what makes an object fall to Earth. The answer, of course, is gravity. But this leads us to more questions: What is gravity? Why do objects attract one another? How does the force of gravity relate to the other forces we experience, such as magnetism?

As physicists attempt to answer these questions they are led to questions of even greater difficulty— and who knows where this particular one may end? Fortunately, most physicists today are not particularly concerned with finding an answer to every single question about nature; they are far more interested in throwing themselves into these problems and seeing just how deep into the hole they can go. The excitement of physics, like any great adventure, comes from unveiling ever greater mysteries, and in physics, there seems to be no end in sight!

A Brief History of Physics

Though ancient physicists did some important work in Greece and the Middle East, the study of physics really begins around the sixteenth century. The astronomical work of Nicolaus Copernicus, Johannes Kepler, and Galileo Galilei paved the way toward a new way of looking at science itself: observation, experiment, and scientific reasoning superseded previously held biases and beliefs.

In the seventeenth century, Sir Isaac Newton changed the world of science forever. He improved on Galileo's work in mechanics (the science of moving things), discovered the law of gravitation, and invented calculus (the form of mathematics on which modern theoretical physics depends). He inspired other scientists to believe that nature could be tamed, studied, and put to use.

Throughout the eighteenth and nineteenth centuries, Newton's work remained the most important ever performed in physics. Even when scientists like Michael Faraday and James Clerk Maxwell finally began to tame the phenomenon of electrical force, they did so within the confines of the physical laws that Newton had already set forth.

Newton saw the universe as a massive mechanical machine (a "clockwork universe," it is often called) which operates under a very precise and predictable set of rules. Understand the rules well enough and nothing would remain a mystery, as everything—living or dead, man or machine—worked like a giant clock, wound up at the beginning of time and set in motion, either by God or by nature.

Kepler

Copernicus

Galileo

Sir Isaac Newton
An obsessive personality, Newton took the same thorough approach to everything he undertook, from alchemy to prosecuting counterfeiters.

"Science cannot solve the ultimate mystery of nature. And that is because, in the last analysis, we ourselves are part of nature and therefore part of the mystery that we are trying to solve."

—**Max Planck**

The Twentieth Century

The Newtonian universe was shattered beyond all recognition in the twentieth century. Albert Einstein, still young and practically unknown, introduced the world to the theory of relativity in 1905. Things that Newton had taken as absolute, such as space and time, were now called into question. According to Einstein, time could speed up and slow down, and an object's length could expand and contract along with the very fabric of space-time!

A decade later, Einstein would even rewrite Newton's theory of gravitation, developing an even more perfect theory in which gravity was caused by the continual "warping" of the very fabric of space-time. A scientific revolution had begun!

The second stage of the revolution came in the form of quantum physics. Based on a relatively simple theory developed by the German scientist Max Planck in 1900, further refined by Einstein, Niels Bohr, and others during the 1900s and 1910s, by the 1920s this entirely new system of physics had shattered the notion of a "clockwork" universe entirely.

These new physicists realized, to the world's utter surprise, that exploring matter more deeply did not lead to more precision, as Newton must have hoped, but less. Where particles exist, nothing is determined—a notion embodied in Werner Heisenberg's famous uncertainty principle (see p. 112).

The rise of quantum physics led to entirely new ways of looking at physics and to new methods of performing calculations and making predictions. These new methods led to the discovery of some very peculiar things: the concept of antimatter; the realization that even some of the smallest particles within atoms are actually made up of even smaller particles; the discovery

GREAT ACHIEVEMENTS IN MODERN PHYSICS

1514	1632	1687	1802	1861
Nicolaus Copernicus begins work on a "Sun-centered" model of the universe.	Galileo Galilei publishes *Dialogue Concerning the Two Chief World Systems*, popularizing the Copernican Theory.	Isaac Newton publishes *Philosophiæ Naturalis Principia Mathematica*, providing the world with his laws of motion and gravitation, and a fully functional theory of physics.	John Dalton discovers the atom.	James Clerk Maxwell provides a mathematical description of light.

The first half of the twentieth century was a period of unparalleled scientific advance, with the likes of Albert Einstein (front row, center), Niels Bohr, and Werner Heisenberg leading the charge.

that our universe is filled with a mysterious substance known as "dark matter"; and much more.

But perhaps the most important revelation is that, at the smallest levels, the universe is not determined. The behaviors of particles are not predictable, because their movements are based on nothing more than probability. Some people have likened quantum physics to Eastern religions or Platonic philosophy, but in the end it is just one more reminder that no matter how much we think we may know, there will always be mysteries yet to uncover in the universe. No wonder, then, that the study of physics is so fascinating!

1896	1900	1905	1913	1927
Henri Becquerel discovers radioactivity.	Max Planck "invents" quantum physics.	Albert Einstein's "miracle year": discovery of theory of relativity and refinement of quantum physics.	Niels Bohr applies quantum physics to the atomic model and founds modern quantum mechanics.	Werner Heisenberg's uncertainty principle is unveiled.

Ancient Physics

Although they did not use the term "scientists," the philosophers of ancient Greece in its golden age, and those of the Middle East and beyond, proved themselves to be thinkers of the highest caliber. This chapter offers a brief guide to those brilliant minds who endeavored to answer many of the same questions that continue to drive the study of physics today—questions of substance, motion, and our place in the universe.

Thales

A search for the first ever scientist (although until a couple of centuries ago they were known as "natural philosophers") can only lead to Thales of Miletus (ca. 624–546 BCE). Thales was one of the "Seven Sages of Greece" and the founder of the first known philosophical "school." Located on the coastline of modern-day Turkey in the Ionian city of Miletus (from which it took its name), the Milesian school and its students became the cornerstone of early scientific thought.

Thales and his Pupils

Thales and his fellow philosophers—most notably two of his students, Anaximander (ca. 610–546 BCE) and Anaximenes (ca. 585–525 BCE)—came up with the first theories of the material universe. The essence of their matter theory was the search for the "quintessential material substance"—what the Greeks called the *arche*. By today's standards, their search was not a practical one. They were not searching for the truth of matter so that they could better understand subjects like chemistry or biology for everyday use, but instead took a more philosophical approach.

• Thales considered that the essential substance was water, for in his observations water played an essential role in the formation of all other types of matter.

• To Anaximander the essential substance was a theoretical material, which he called *apeiron* (Greek for "infinite").

• To Anaximenes it was air.

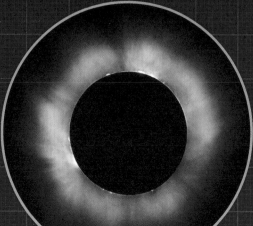

At the heart of the Milesian theory was the idea of change: if all could be reduced to a single substance, then there had to be a constant and unstoppable change taking place within matter in order to transform one element into another. With the Milesians, science and philosophy first began intermingling.

Further Contributions

Though the details of his life are cloudy at best, it can be said with some certainty that Thales was the first in a long line of prominent Greek thinkers. In addition to his theories of matter (which played an essential role in spurring on the great debate that quickly followed on this subject), Thales was the first to encourage the Greek world to seek out natural explanations for phenomena, rather than seeking answers only from faith or mysticism.

At the same time he made great strides in mathematics, particularly in practical geometry, three centuries before Euclid would develop the first full system of geometrical proofs. As one of the earliest astronomers, it is said that Thales predicted the solar eclipse that brought to a halt a battle between the Lydians and the Medes.

OPPONENTS OF THALES

Parmenides (early fifth century BCE) believed that change is impossible, illogical, and illusory. His ideas influenced later philosophers such as Democritus, Plato, and Zeno of Elea.

Zeno of Elea (mid-fifth century BCE) invented a number of logical paradoxes to prove that change is impossible. It was not until the development of calculus in the seventeenth century that Zeno's paradoxes could finally be solved.

Melissus of Samos (fifth century BCE) stressed the importance of believing in the physical world as constant, rather than changing. He referred to everything that exists as "The One."

"Philosophy begins with Thales."
—**Bertrand Russell**

The eclipse of the Sun that Thales predicted is thought to have happened on May 28, 585 BCE. It is possibly the earliest historical event that has a precisely known date. The two warring armies regarded the eclipse as a message from the gods, and decided to call a truce.

The First Theories of Matter

One question dominated debate between Greek philosophers and scientists in ancient times: What is matter? These thinkers desired to understand physical reality at its most basic level, asking questions about the very substance from which everything was made. Were there many elements which combined to form matter, or was it all just one? Was matter made of atoms or fluids?

The Atomists

Democritus did most of his work between about 440 and 400 BCE. Though he is best remembered today for his forward-looking theory of "atoms" (which comes from the Greek word for "uncuttable"), he was known in his own day as the "laughing philosopher" for the cheerfulness and optimism expressed in his philosophy (the vast majority of which is now lost).

Democritus used the image of a sandy beach to explain his theory of atoms. Just as the tiny grains of sand when viewed from afar look like a single substance, so all matter might be made up of tiny little granules of matter. The smallest of these pieces of matter he called "atoms."

Though we know now that there is some truth in Democritus' theory, his work was not so easy to accept at the time, especially as other, apparently more logical theories existed. This first atomic theory would be neglected for more than 2,000 years before being picked up again by the likes of Galileo Galilei and Isaac Newton, and it was not fully accepted until well into the nineteenth century.

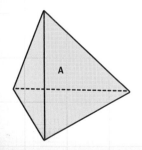
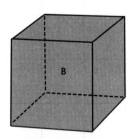
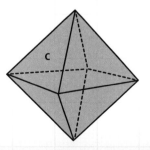

The Elementalists

Most Greeks preferred the rival theory of Empedocles. He believed that matter consisted of just four primary elements: earth, fire, air, and water. This in itself was not a new idea, but Empedocles developed it into a expansive theory. He saw change not as the rearrangement of tiny atoms, but as the mixing and separating of the four elements. These processes were driven by two opposite forces, which he called love and strife. The force of love bound elements together, while strife tore them apart. How poetic!

Plato's Solids

It was the legendary Plato, born around 428 BCE (not long after Empedocles' death), who advanced this theory by introducing the idea of "Platonic solids."

Plato was the master of deductive argumentation—beginning with a general point and logically narrowing his thoughts in order to come to a specific conclusion. He tried to explain Empedocles' theory through the science of geometry.

Most Greeks agreed with Empedocles that matter consisted of just four primary elements: earth, fire, air, and water.

Plato looked at the four elements of Empedocles and determined that each of these might be represented by a geometrical figure (figures A, B, C, and E below).

Plato argued that the four elements were not continuous substances, as Empedocles had implied, but were, as in atomic theory, made of tiny invisible particles. These particles were geometrical shapes, and the sizes and peculiar shapes of these particles were the cause of the vast differences between one element and another.

The Platonic solids are the only shapes that can be constructed whose faces, sides, and angles are all identical to one another. Plato assigned each solid (except the dodecahedron) to one of the elements.

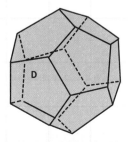

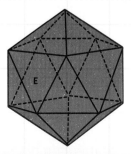

A = tetrahedron (triangular pyramid): fire

B = hexahedron (cube): earth

C = octahedron (8 sides): air

D = dodecahedron (12 sides)

E = icosahedron (20 sides): water

Aristotle

Possibly the most important philosopher in all of antiquity, Aristotle's vast catalog of works covers a prodigious range of subjects, from biology and physics to medicine and theology. While many of his works were filled with brilliant insights and original research (especially in areas such as biology and moral philosophy), it was in his unique ability to outline and clarify science as a whole that Aristotle surely had the greatest impact on the course of physics in the western world.

A Remarkable Life

Aristotle was born and raised in the town of Stageira, in the eastern Greek province of Chalcidice, around 384 BCE. At 18 years old, Aristotle joined the Academy, Plato's famed school for thinkers in Athens, where he remained for nearly two decades until the death of his teacher. Because of his time there, much of Aristotle's thinking on philosophy closely resembles that of Plato, although he certainly went far beyond his teacher in many subjects.

▶ KEY WORKS

ORGANON (LOGIC): A collection of six fundamental works on logic which constitutes a full, structured system of reasoning.

PHYSICS: Aristotle's broad, far-reaching attempt at explaining all natural phenomena in a single work; an application of his methods of logic to the material world.

METAPHYSICS: One of the most important philosophical works in history, *Metaphysics* goes beyond *Physics* by asking deeper questions about the nature of existence, cause, and change. Aristotle argues that all physical objects are made up of two elements: form and matter.

The Aether: Aristotle believed in a fifth element called "quintessence" or "aether," a universal, all-encompassing substance in which all other elements exist, and which holds the heavenly bodies in the sky. Parts of this theory persisted even into the twentieth century.

father, Alexander took the throne and proceeded to conquer much of the known world. So great was the empire of Aristotle's prized student that his eventual death would cause great chaos and social upheaval, extending throughout most of the Mediterranean world and beyond. The death of Alexander is seen by many historians as the end of the "classical" period of Greek history, and of the great age of philosophy in the fifth and fourth centuries BCE.

Aristotle's Physics

Aristotle's works covered a vast range of subjects, building on the theories of past philosophers while at the same time developing entirely new (and quite revolutionary) ideas from the ground up. He explored such things as the origins of the universe, light, optical phenomena, mathematics, biology (he developed one of the first systems for classifying plants and animals), medicine, and much more.

So venerated was Aristotle that his contributions to western philosophy (even those contributions which were entirely incorrect) would remain mostly unchallenged for nearly 2,000 years.

Leaving the Academy and the city-state of Athens behind, Aristotle traveled to Asia Minor (Anatolia), where he studied botany and zoology. He was soon invited by King Philip II of Macedon to become personal tutor to his son, a young man named Alexander—later to be known as Alexander the Great.

Aristotle's new student did not become a famous philosopher himself, but he certainly did have an impact upon the whole of western civilization. After the death of his

ETHICS AND *POLITICS*: Like many of the philosophers who followed him, Aristotle focused largely on questions of ethics and morality. He argued that a person can become virtuous only by behaving virtuously. In short, he regarded ethics as a practical, rather than theoretical, pursuit.

Archimedes

Though many philosophers in ancient Greece preferred questions of abstract theory, Archimedes was a scientist of the most practical kind. While others considered the nature of matter and existence, he attempted to get a better understanding of the world through mathematics and through the principles of simple machines—devices that took advantage of physical laws in order to make work easier. Some of these machines had been in use from the earliest days of human civilization, but Archimedes sought to improve upon them by applying newly developed scientific and mathematical principles.

The Practical Philosopher

Archimedes was born in Syracuse, Sicily, around 287 BCE. Greece at this time consisted of independent city-states, and Archimedes was a citizen of Magna Grecia, the Greek-controlled region of what is today southern Italy.

Archimedes' father is said to have been an astronomer named Phidias. Perhaps it was from him that

Archimedes received his unceasing interest in nearly every scientific and mathematical subject. Sadly, Archimedes' brilliance could not save him during the Roman invasion of Syracuse in 212 BCE. He is said to have been killed by a Roman soldier as he studied a mathematical diagram that he had drawn upon the dust of his floor. According to legend, the great man's last words were: "Do not disturb my circles."

"Give me a place to stand and I shall move the world," Archimedes is supposed to have said. The lever is one of the simplest of all machines, and Archimedes imagined himself somewhere in the farthest reaches of space, using a fantastically long lever to move the planet.

greatly improved upon the ancient idea of the catapult and designed other military weapons, including a heat ray to burn enemy ships.

The Science of Archimedes

A great mathematician, Archimedes is known as the father of integral calculus and one of the first people to calculate the value of pi. But he is best remembered for his discovery of the principle of buoyancy.

A new golden crown had been made for King Hiero II of Syracuse, but there was reason to suspect that it had been made partly of silver, rather than pure gold. Archimedes had to find out the composition of the crown without destroying it. The problem was that the density of the crown could only be calculated by measuring its volume and its weight, yet because the crown's shape was so irregular, no exact calculation of its volume could be made. As the story goes, Archimedes was taking a bath when he realized that he could calculate the volume of his body by measuring the displacement of the water in the tub. Realizing that he could use this same method to calculate the volume of the crown, the legend goes that Archimedes leaped from the bath and ran naked through the streets shouting *Eureka!* ("I've found it!")

ARCHIMEDES THE INVENTOR

As a practical scientist of the first order, Archimedes is known for his many ingenious inventions, which include Archimedes' screw.

This simple device consists of a screw-shaped blade within a hollow cylinder. When the screw is rotated, liquid can be carried from one end of the cylinder to the other.

It is said that Archimedes invented the screw in order to remove the bilge water from the bottom of Greek vessels. It is still used today to drain flooded land and also to irrigate crops.

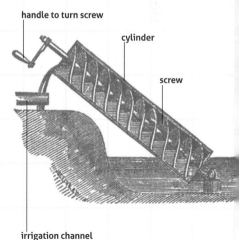

handle to turn screw

cylinder

screw

irrigation channel

Science in the Dark Ages

By the second century BCE, the prime position
enjoyed by ancient Greek civilization had waned.
This was followed by more than 1,500 years of scientific
stagnation in the Western world. During this period,
many of the great works of antiquity were neglected
and eventually lost forever. Many important works
were lost as a result of the repeated destruction of the
great Library of Alexandria (which had to be rebuilt
multiple times) during the first few centuries CE.
Fortunately, however, the key ideas from this period
survived the destruction.

The Fall of the West

When the Western Roman Empire
fell, not only had Democritus' theory
of tiny particles (atoms) been long
since discarded, but even the legacy
of Aristotle, the greatest thinker of
them all, was in danger of being
forgotten entirely. The Roman world
was not wholly without scientists:
Ptolemy, for example, in the second
century CE, was considered one of
the finest astronomers of his day,
offering up an incorrect, though still
rather brilliant Earth-centered

model of the solar system. But Europe
was beginning its steady decline into
that period known as the Middle Ages
(a term generally assigned to the
thousand or so years following the fall
of the Western Roman Empire in the
fifth century CE). Questions of science
were no longer felt to be important.

A Light in the Darkness

Fortunately for the modern world,
within the growing Arab communities
of Persia and the Middle East a few
notable figures were able to shed
some scientific light on these "dark
ages." The eleventh-century scholar
Abu Ali al-Hasan ibn al-Hasan ibn
al-Haytham (commonly referred to in
the West as Alhazen) possessed a
particularly brilliant scientific mind.
He carried out some formidable
studies on the subject of light—a
phenomenon that had been even
more elusive than atoms to the
ancient thinkers.

> When the Western Roman
> Empire fell, even the
> legacy of Aristotle, the
> greatest thinker of them all,
> was in danger of being
> forgotten entirely.

Alhazen is often known today as "the father of optics." He was one of the first thinkers to utilize a truly inductive scientific method—one that begins with experiment and then develops theories based on these observations. Alhazen performed experiments using lenses and mirrors to produce some of the first calculations of light reflection and refraction. He also explored the separation of light into its constituent colors using a prism.

Although he is remembered in large part for his work on optics, during his career Alhazen also performed exciting work in mathematics, astronomy, medicine, and even psychology. It would be several more centuries before his work was known and appreciated in the West.

Other Arab Scholars of the Dark Ages

Alhazen was not alone. Ali ibn Isa, in the tenth century, explored the optical part of the brain and made a highly accurate measurement of the Earth's circumference. Al-Battani, in the ninth century, made corrections to Ptolemy's astronomical tables and made numerous contributions to mathematics. Above all, Arab and Persian scholars translated many ancient Greek works into Arabic, thus preserving them for the benefit of the entire world.

ALHAZEN'S BOOK OF OPTICS

Though Alhazen is credited as being the author of more than 200 scientific and mathematical works (about half of which have survived), one stands out as his most memorable: the *Book of Optics*. In this work, Alhazen describes optical phenomena in greater detail than had ever been accomplished before. Over the course of seven books he looks at how light travels, how images are perceived by the eye, how light can be altered and changed by way of reflection, refraction, or diffraction, and much more. It is truly one of the great scientific works of all time.

An etching of **Alhazen**, as he was known in the West.

The First Photographs

It is remarkably easy to take pictures today. Since the advent of digital photography, there really is nothing to it. Just point, click, review, delete, and repeat the steps all over again *ad nauseam*. The entire process takes only seconds and no expensive film is wasted. Looking back just a few years, before the takeover of digital technology, taking pictures was a much more time-consuming and expensive process. Imagine, then, what it must have been like 900 years ago, when the first ever camera was invented.

The First Camera

In the eleventh century, the Persian scientist Alhazen (see pp. 22–23) created a remarkably simple, yet fascinating invention: a small room, closed off to all light except for a tiny hole in one wall. A cone of light filtered through this hole to project images of the outside world onto the opposite wall of the room, as if a snapshot had been taken.

Alhazen used these projected images as a basis for further scientific inquiry. It wasn't until the sixteenth century that artists began to use the device as a tool for capturing images of the world. Placing a piece of paper or canvas on the wall, they could trace the image that appeared inside the dark room, creating uncannily realistic representations of the outside world.

In 1826, French inventor Joseph-Nicéphore Niépce took the first permanent photograph, using the principles of the camera obscura and his own knowledge of chemistry. In Niépce's invention, the image that arrived in the camera became embedded onto a pewter plate covered with various chemicals, thus fixing the image. Thirty-five years later, in 1861, Scottish physicist James Clerk Maxwell (see pp. 60–61) took the first durable color photograph. He took three shots using filters of different colors and then projected the three images on top of one another.

The English word "camera" comes from the Latin term used to describe the very first piece of photographic equipment: *camera obscura*, or "dark room."

BUILD YOUR OWN CAMERA OBSCURA

Many photographers and hobbyists today continue to experiment with photography by building their own pinhole cameras, using the principles of the camera obscura as outlined by Alhazen more than 1,000 years ago.

projected image of object

lightproof box

object

shutter

The **lightproof box** or camera obscura need be nothing more than a cardboard box, with its joints sealed with opaque adhesive tape.

The pinhole is best made in a piece of metal foil. Cut a window in the cardboard box and tape the foil inside.

The shutter is a flap of card, hinged with adhesive tape to the front of the box. Open the shutter to begin the exposure, then tape it shut when the exposure is finished. You will have to use trial and error to find out how long to leave the shutter open.

pinhole

photographic paper

Pinhole cameras have been made from all sorts of things, from matchboxes to trash cans, but a cardboard box is the simplest way to start. There are numerous resources online and at local libraries which describe in simple terms how to construct these fun devices. The smaller and neater the pinhole, the sharper the image will be, though it will never be quite as sharp as the image from a lens. The photographic paper is taped to the inside of the box, opposite the pinhole. The image on the paper appears upside down because the rays of light from the object cross over as they pass through the pinhole.

2

The
Renaissance
Begins

The Renaissance (French for "rebirth") was a period of significant progress in both arts and sciences. This was the age of Leonardo da Vinci and Michelangelo, and many other brilliant and original minds. This chapter introduces the groundbreaking theories of Copernicus, Galileo, and others—theories that helped instigate the study of science as we know it. By asking new questions, these scientists began to offer real answers and to establish the scientific method that we still use today.

Nicolaus Copernicus

Nicolaus Copernicus ushered in a new era of scientific thought with his work *De Revolutionibus Orbium Coelestium* (*On the Revolutions of the Heavenly Spheres*). By asserting that the planets revolve around the Sun, Copernicus brought about a true revolution in European science. It is for this reason that Copernicus is often credited as being one of the first to attempt to bring science out of the Dark Ages and into the Renaissance— the "rebirth of learning."

The Monastic Astronomer

Copernicus is thought of as the founder of modern astronomy. He was born in Poland on February 19, 1473, and, after his father's death, was raised by his uncle, Lucas Watzenrode. Copernicus never married, but devoted his long life to religion and to a wide range of scientific studies.

After studying mathematics and optics at Kraków University, Copernicus moved on to Bologna, Italy, where he studied church law. His schooling complete, Copernicus returned to Poland to work as secretary to his uncle, who was now Prince-Bishop of Warmia.

Though he had wide-ranging interests (including art and languages such as Greek and Latin), Copernicus soon began to concentrate on astronomy. Because the telescope had yet to be invented, he had to make his observations with the naked eye, from a turret on the wall surrounding his home.

Copernicus died in Frombork (Frauenburg) on May 24, 1543. A frequently repeated legend has it that his most famous and groundbreaking book, *On the Revolutions of the Heavenly Spheres*, was published on his final day, and the completed work was presented to him just before he died.

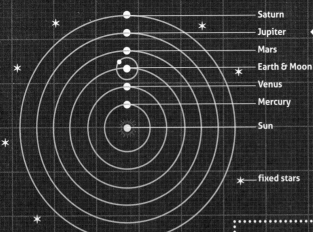

Saturn
Jupiter
Mars
Earth & Moon
Venus
Mercury
Sun

fixed stars

The Copernican model of our Solar System consisted of eight spheres: six for the known planets orbiting the Sun, one for the Moon orbiting Earth, and one final sphere for the distant stars.

" At rest, however, in the middle of everything is the Sun. "

—Copernicus

A Revolutionary Idea about Revolutions

As early as 1514, Copernicus had been laying the groundwork for the heliocentric (Sun-centered) theory of the universe. Although it did not immediately supplant the reigning Ptolemaic (Earth-centered) system, it provided the foundation upon which later thinkers such as Kepler (see pp. 30–31) and Galileo (pp. 34–35) could construct their own theories.

The new theory involved a system of eight "spheres," or orbits, based on a tremendous number of precise calculations compiled by Copernicus and published after his death. Six of these spheres represented the orbits of the planets known at the time—Mercury, Venus, Earth, Mars, Jupiter, and Saturn—and had the Sun at their center. The seventh was the outermost sphere (the "firmament") upon which the distant stars sat. The remaining sphere was the orbit of the Moon, with the Earth as its central point.

KEY WORKS

ON THE REVOLUTIONS OF THE HEAVENLY SPHERES:
Published in 1543, this work represents a defining moment in the history of science, for it is the first major work published which argued strongly for a heliocentric model of the Solar System. Copernicus not only explained, piece by piece over the course of six books, the revolutions of each of the planets and the movements of the Sun and Moon; he also provided detailed explanations of how the positions of astronomical objects can be calculated. This enabled his theory to be verified by way of prediction and experimentation. It was thus the first truly "scientific" theory of astronomy.

Tycho Brahe & Johannes Kepler

Tycho Brahe and Johannes Kepler were brilliant men in their own individual ways. Brahe had an insatiable desire to understand the motions of objects in space, which led him to make some of the most important measurements of planetary motions, while Kepler had a unique mathematical mind which could interpret tables of data in order to find consistent patterns in the midst of seeming chaos. Together, they ushered in a new era of astronomy and physics.

The Noseless Dane

The Danish nobleman Tycho Brahe (1546–1601) became enthralled with the idea of astronomy from a very young age, impressed by the fact that astronomers, even as far back as the sixth century BCE, could not only observe but predict events in the night sky.

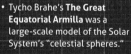
Tycho Brahe's **The Great Equatorial Armilla** was a large-scale model of the Solar System's "celestial spheres."

a clairvoyant dwarf (whom he kept under his dinner table), and domesticate a moose (that later died after drinking too much beer and falling down the stairs).

Brahe (pictured below) aimed to improve astronomy by amassing a huge wealth of observational data, but only after a rather riotous youth, which saw him lose his nose in a duel (he famously sported a false nose made of gold, silver, and wax), hire

After discovering a new star and publishing a book on it, Tycho was given land by the Danish King, Frederick II, to build Uraniborg, the world's foremost astronomical observatory. He built a "Great Equatorial Armilla" (a model of the celestial spheres) some 9 feet (2.75 m) across; his "Great Mural Quadrant" (an instrument used to measure the exact locations of heavenly bodies) was 13 feet (4 m) across. After a disagreement with Frederick II, Brahe moved to Prague, where he was appointed imperial astronomer.

Brahe never came to accept the Copernican model of a heliocentric universe; instead, he chose to interpret his massive quantities of data using the old Earth-centered model. It remained to be seen whether the data could support his view of the universe.

The Mercenary's Son

Johannes Kepler (pictured right) was born near Stuttgart, Germany, in 1571, the son of a mercenary soldier and an innkeeper's daughter (who, it is said, was tried for witchcraft). A small, frail man with poor eyesight but remarkable intelligence, Kepler won a scholarship allowing him to attend the University of Tübingen.

Young Kepler sought to combine Copernicus' observations with the geometry he was learning in school. He followed mathematical clues to devise his own model in which the orbits of the six known planets lay on the surfaces of six spheres, each of which could be fitted into one of Plato's perfect solids (see p. 17), from an octahedron for Mercury's orbit to a cube for Saturn. Although Kepler's theory turned out to be wrong, the model impressed Brahe enough that he invited the young man to work with him. Eighteen months later, Brahe died of an acute urinary infection. His last words to his assistant, reportedly, were, "Let me not seem to have lived in vain."

Kepler was named Brahe's successor as imperial mathematician and given the responsibility of completing Brahe's unfinished work. His superb mathematical skills allowed him to calculate the orbits of the planets more accurately, leading to the discovery that the planetary orbits are not circles but ellipses.

Further research led Kepler to establish three laws of planetary orbits that would fundamentally change the science of astronomy, inspiring future generations of scientists including Galileo (see pp. 34–35) and Newton (pp. 44–45).

KEY WORKS

MYSTERIUM COSMO-GRAPHICUM (1596): In his first major astronomical work, *The Cosmographic Mystery*, Kepler outlines his geometrical theory of planetary orbits.

ASTRONOMIAE PARS OPTICA (1604): *The Optical Part of Astronomy* is one of the founding works in the field of optics. Kepler also applied his understanding of optics to the human eye.

ASTRONOMIA NOVA (1609): In *New Astronomy*, Kepler lays out the laws of planetary motion, leading to his new discovery that the planets move along elliptical orbits.

Kepler's Laws of Planetary Motion

Johannes Kepler's greatest achievement was to develop three brief laws that defined the movement of every known astronomical body in the Solar System—laws that are still used by astronomers and physicists today, four centuries after their discovery. The three laws are remarkably simple.

The First Law

> The orbits of the planets are elliptical, with the Sun as one of the points of focus of each one.

Unlike a circle, which has only one point at its center, an ellipse has two centers, or "foci." Kepler realized that the paths of the planets were not perfect circles, with the Sun as a sole point of focus, but ellipses, with the Sun as one of two focal points. What is at the other point? It is, in a sense, the overall gravitational attraction of everything else in the Solar System, which combines to turn circular orbits into ellipses.

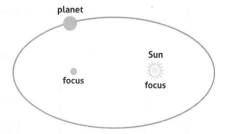

Because of the elliptical nature of orbits, the distance between the Sun and each planet (or between Earth and the Moon) is always changing. There are points along every orbit where the object, or body, is closest to the Sun (this is called the "perihelion") and farthest from the Sun ("aphelion").

The Second Law

> The line joining the planet to the Sun sweeps out equal areas in equal times as the planet moves along its orbit.

This second law requires an element of decoding, although the principle it teaches is beautiful in its simplicity. Space agencies such as NASA use this law to predict the position of a spacecraft at any given moment.

Essentially, this law means that the planet moves faster when it is nearer the Sun. Thus, not only is the distance

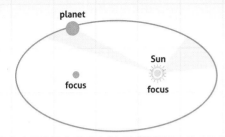

planet

Sun

focus

focus

This principle is perhaps a little simpler when written out in the mathematical form:

$$T^2 \propto O^3$$

In this equation (one of the simplest in all of physics) T represents the period of revolution for a planet and O represents the length of its semi-major axis.

of a planet constantly fluctuating as it orbits the Sun, but its speed constantly changes as well. So the perihelion represents the fastest speed of an orbit, while the aphelion represents the slowest.

The Third Law

The square of the revolutionary period of a planet is proportional to the cube of the semi-major axis of its orbit.

Kepler's third law states simply that the orbital period for a planet around the Sun (in Earth's case, 365 days) increases dramatically with the radius of its orbit.

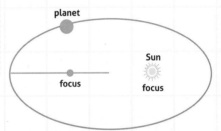

planet

focus

Sun

focus

PLANETARY ORBIT TABLE

	Mean Distance from the Sun	Orbital Period (in Earth Days)
Mercury	36,000,000 miles	87.96 Days
Venus	67,110,000 miles	224.68 Days
Earth	93,000,000 miles	365.26 Days
Mars	141,700,000 miles	686.98 Days
Jupiter	484,400,000 miles	4,329 Days
Saturn	887,900,000 miles	10,751 Days
Uranus	1,784,000,000 miles	30,685 Days
Neptune	2,801,000,000 miles	60,155 Days

Galileo Galilei

Galileo is perhaps the best example of the contrast between the science practiced by ancient scholars and those who took part in the abundant scientific achievements of the European Renaissance. Galileo's achievements include the further popularization of the Copernican model of the cosmos, a scientific explanation of the pendulum, the discovery of the moons of Jupiter, improving the design of the telescope, and helping to develop one of the first real "scientific methods."

The Martyrdom of Galileo

The story is often told of how Galileo angered the Roman Catholic church by insisting that the Earth revolves around the Sun, rather than the other way around. Most people have heard of the threats made against him; how he was forced to recant those views that he had so eloquently laid out in his brilliant book, *Dialogue Concerning the Two Chief World Systems*; and how, in a rousing demonstration of indignation, he muttered under his breath after recanting, "And yet, it does move."

Though these words may be no more than a legend, they illustrate the popular idea of Galileo—that he spent the final years of his life as a martyr to the cause of science. This is true enough, but we must not overlook a life absolutely filled with remarkable discoveries—so many that it is quite impossible to mention all of them here.

The first telescopes magnified distant objects only up to three or four times.

Though Galileo did not invent the telescope, he certainly took advantage of the new technology by improving and popularizing it.

A Renaissance Man

....

Born in 1564 in Pisa, Italy, Galileo is what today may be called a true Renaissance man, for he did not limit himself to one field of study but excelled at a great many. He was, like his father, a musician and a painter. He also studied medicine in his youth.

Galileo discovered the secrets of the pendulum's swing (see pp. 36–37). Then, using primitive timing methods (including his own pulse and the oscillation of a pendulum), he began performing experiments in motion, proving once and for all that bodies of different weights fall at the same speed (see right).

In 1609 Galileo first heard of a new instrument invented by Hans Lippershey in the Netherlands: the telescope. By August of that year Galileo had not only built one himself, but had greatly improved on it. He went on to build some of the best telescopes in the world, which he used to view areas of space that no eye had seen. He discovered Jupiter's moons, the phases of Venus, the rings of Saturn, and much more.

Galileo's brush with the Church did not occur until he was nearly 70 years old. It was the publication of his *Dialogue* in 1632 that caused the trouble. Galileo was ordered to stand trial for heresy, leading him to recant his views. For the last nine years of his life, Galileo lived under house arrest at his home near Florence, where he died in 1642.

FALLING BODIES

For centuries before Galileo, it was believed (following Aristotle) that a heavy object would fall faster than a lighter object. Pick up a feather and a rock, drop the two of them—and the rock will indeed fall faster than the feather.

Galileo understood that this commonsense notion might be an illusion. The feather really does fall more slowly, but this is because there is another force acting on it besides gravity: air resistance.

Galileo considered dropping two objects from the famous Leaning Tower in his home town of Pisa, but air resistance would have spoiled the experiment. Instead, he rolled balls of different weights down inclined planes (ramps). This slowed the balls down so that their speed of descent could be measured. Aristotle was wrong: the balls rolled down the ramp at precisely the same speed, no matter how light or heavy they were.

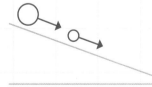

Balls rolling down an inclined plane will move at the same speed regardless of weight.

Pendulum Physics

Pendulums are remarkably simple devices, though they are not put into use as frequently today as they once were. The most common application for pendulums throughout history has been in the mechanism of a clock, where one might see a narrow rod ending in a weight swinging back and forth, driving the complex gears within. What makes the pendulum so useful in keeping time? Galileo Galilei found a rather simple formula to explain the behavior of the pendulum.

A Remarkable Discovery

Any time a string with a weight at the end is swung back and forth, a pendulum is created. A pendulum consists merely of a rod, wire, or string of fixed length from which a weight is suspended (*pendulus* in Latin means "hanging"). The weight is allowed to swing freely back and forth, carried along a fixed path by gravity.

The direction of the swing of a Foucault pendulum rotates slowly clockwise (in the northern hemisphere), completing a full cycle in about a day. The exact time taken depends on the latitude at which the experiment is carried out.

The time it takes for a pendulum to swing in one direction and back again is called the period of oscillation. What determines the period of a pendulum? Its initial speed? How hard it is pushed? The mass of the weight? Galileo discovered that none of these answers are correct. In fact, the period of a pendulum is dependent on only one factor: its length.

As the story goes, Galileo observed the swinging of a chandelier and timed its periods using his pulse. To his great surprise, the period remained constant—even as the chandelier's movement slowed, its period remained the same.

Galileo suddenly had access to a simple device which could allow him to keep time with much more accuracy than his own pulse. Within a few decades of Galileo's death, the Dutch physicist

Christiaan Huygens had developed a mathematical equation which defined the period of the pendulum. It was not long before pendulums were partnered with systems of gears, wheels, and moving hands to produce the first truly accurate timekeeping devices.

A Foucault pendulum at the North or South Pole should have a rotation period of 24 hours. This was confirmed by an experiment in 2001.

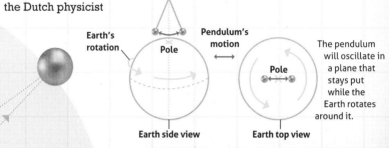

Earth's rotation
Pole
Pendulum's motion
Pole
The pendulum will oscillate in a plane that stays put while the Earth rotates around it.

Earth side view   **Earth top view**

FOUCAULT'S PENDULUM

Gravity, the very thing that keeps a pendulum in motion, also determines the speed and direction of its swing. In 1851, Léon Foucault created a massive pendulum which was free to swing in any direction, and as it did so it traced lines in a bed of fine sand. After he had set it in motion, Foucault demonstrated that the pendulum had turned slowly in a clockwise direction. (This movement is called "precession.") Since the vertical plane in which a pendulum swings does not change once it has been set in motion, the tracings proved once and for all that Earth must be turning.

René Descartes

René Descartes is remembered today for his achievements in various fields, from pure sciences and mathematics to the most abstract philosophy. Though a contemporary of Galileo, Descartes was not so singularly focused on performing experiments and developing concrete scientific theories. His focus was on determining precisely how one should endeavor to think about things in the first place. He thought and wrote about logic, about method, and about how one might finally come to understand the universe in full.

A Traveling Scholar

Descartes was born in 1596 and educated at the Jesuit college of La Flèche in Anjou, France. He entered the college at only eight years old, studying the basic (and mostly unquestioned) tenets of Aristotelian philosophy and essential mathematics. From a young age, Descartes suffered from poor health and from this he developed the lifelong habit of remaining in bed each day until late morning.

After graduating from La Flèche in 1612, Descartes traveled restlessly throughout Europe. He gained a law degree, attended military school, and studied mathematics extensively.

By 1628, weary of traveling, he settled in Holland, where he wrote his physics treatise *The World*. In this book Descartes states that matter is made up of tiny "corpuscles" (a precursor to modern atomic theory) and describes a universe in which Earth moves around the Sun.

KEY WORKS

LE MONDE (1664): *The World* was written in 1628 but published posthumously in 1664. It is Descartes' first thorough presentation of his natural philosophy and includes a description of atoms and an account of the Copernican Solar System.

DISCOURS DE LA MÉTHODE (1637): In *Discourse on Method* Descartes seeks to unify all scientific, mathe-matical, and philosophical topics by way of reason. The work set the bench-mark for "modern" scientific practice.

MEDITATIONES DE PRIMA PHILOSOPHIA (1641): *Meditations on First Philosophy* describes Descartes' dualistic philosophy, in which he argues that the human mind is separate from the body, and that our thoughts confirm our own reality.

PRINCIPIA PHILOSOPHIAE (1644): *Principles of Philosophy* lays out Descartes' thoughts on natural philosophy, including his assertion that, free from external forces, the motion of an object will be constant and follow a straight line. Descartes intended this book to be a radical departure from the curriculum taught in western European universities, particularly in Britain and France.

Descartes offered a now famous explanation as to how one might know that they exist: **"I think, therefore I am."**

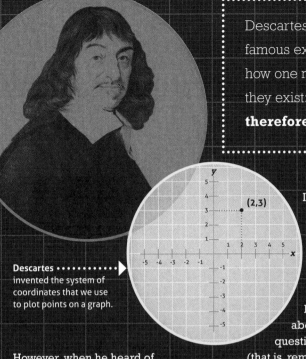

Descartes •••••••••• invented the system of coordinates that we use to plot points on a graph.

In his monumental *Discourse on Method*, published in 1637, Descartes began with simple principles and taught his readers how best to think about science, first by questioning everything (that is, removing all bias) and then building up a theory based on sound observation. Descartes also used this work to invent one of the most common tools in all of mathematics: the Cartesian coordinate system.

However, when he heard of Galileo's troubles in Italy, he decided not to publish the work.

The Method of Science

Descartes tackled deep philosophical questions about truth and the nature of humanity from a purely logical perspective. He also set about devising a comprehensive plan for combining science and mathematics to produce a more objective framework for the development of human knowledge. Though he did not deny the basic tenets of religion, Descartes believed that pure science and reason were all one needed in order to understand fully the workings of the universe.

Descartes moved into more abstractly philosophical territory in *Meditations on First Philosophy* (1641), where he offered his famous explanation as to how one might know that they exist: "I think, therefore I am."

Descartes died of pneumonia in Stockholm in 1650; Queen Christina of Sweden had persuaded him to move there in order to become her personal tutor.

The Scientific Method

During the Renaissance, European scholars were responsible for advancing human understanding of theories such as motion, gravitation, and optics, as well as forging new ground in areas such as mathematical physics. Perhaps the single most important of these, however, was the development of a clear, concise, and consistent scientific method—a system by which both observation and reason were employed in order to test more rigorously the theories of the universe.

The Steps of the Scientific Method

Although there is no single defined series of steps by which every scientist conducts research, there is at least a generally agreed method which constitutes good practice. It tends to go something like this:

1 Make an observation about the universe: for example, a hiker walking through a forest spots two black bears.

2 Describe this observation and use it to develop a general rule, called a hypothesis, that is consistent with the observation: the hiker thinks to herself, "Those bears are black, so all bears must be black."

3 Use the hypothesis to make predictions about future experiments: the hiker predicts that when she sees another bear, it will also be black, as will the bear following that one.

4 Test those predictions by performing experiments and making further observations. Be prepared to modify the hypothesis in the light of these latest results: the hiker sees that the next bear is brown—she amends her hypothesis to include brown bears as well as black bears.

Finding Truth in Science

There is no real last step to this basic scientific method, unfortunately. The nature of science is such that these steps must repeat endlessly, and the truth is that in science one really never can take the final step and declare something a "fact."

A theory may only be as complete as the experimentation that is used to develop it—thus, when we say something like "The force of gravity is felt between any two objects in the universe," what we have is only a theory—it is a generalized

5 Repeat the pattern of observation and refinement of the hypothesis until there are no longer any discrepancies (the hiker travels all over the world, and has soon enough found black bears, brown bears, white bears, black-and-white bears, gray bears, and bears of a few other colors; eventually she has expanded her hypothesis to include every bear she could find on Earth). The greater the number of accurate observations, the more accurate the hypothesis. This is the foundation of the scientific method.

OCCAM'S RAZOR

Occam's razor is a logical principle attributed to the fourteenth-century friar William of Ockham that has become a hallmark of scientific theories ever since.

Occam stated that "Entities should not be multiplied unnecessarily." This has been taken to mean that wherever two or more explanations exist for a given phenomenon, the simpler one is generally preferable. In other words, scientists use Occam's "razor" to cut away any superfluous elements of a theory, preferring to leave only the simplest explanation necessary. Logic dictates that the simpler answer tends to be preferable to an overly complicated one. This little rule is useful in any logical situation, even outside the realm of science.

prediction based on what we have so far observed about our universe. Perhaps one day we might find that somewhere in a distant galaxy there are objects which do not obey the law of gravity. If we did, we would recognize that our theory was incomplete and we would have our work cut out trying to fix it.

The development of a clear, concise, and consistent scientific method was the single most important achievement of Renaissance scholars.

3

The Birth of
Modern
Physics

Beginning with the groundbreaking work of Isaac Newton toward the end of the seventeenth century, this chapter focuses on many of the essential elements of "Newtonian" physics. Newton's work laid the foundations for the physical sciences for well over 200 years and it continues to guide our understanding of the universe to this day. This chapter gives an account of the theories of motion, gravitation, thermodynamics, and many of the other essential building blocks of modern physics.

Isaac Newton

Isaac Newton surely possessed one of the greatest minds in history. His achievements can hardly be overstated, either in the pure sciences (the laws of force and gravity bear his name), mathematics (he invented calculus), theology (a lifelong passion), alchemy (perhaps his favorite subject), or any number of other interests. Newton's work represents a transition from the science of the Renaissance to a truly "modern" scientific approach.

A Difficult Personality

Isaac Newton was born on Christmas Day 1642 in the small hamlet of Woolsthorpe-by-Colsterworth, Lincolnshire, England. His father, a successful farmer, died before Isaac was born. Newton was famously difficult to get along with and emotionally unstable, but his brilliance overshadowed all of this.

> "No great discovery was ever made without a bold guess."
>
> —Isaac Newton

In 1665, after graduating from Cambridge University, he returned home to avoid an outbreak of plague. Here he made some of his most memorable contributions, including the development of calculus, a revolutionary theory of light and color, and an attempt to explain planetary motion (though it is not clear whether the famous "falling apple" incident really happened). The work done during these years eventually led to Newton's single greatest work, *Philosophiæ Naturalis Principia Mathematica* (*Mathematical Principles of Natural Philosophy*), published in 1687. He returned to Cambridge in 1667 and eventually became Lucasian Professor of Mathematics there.

KEY WORKS

PHILOSOPHIAE NATURALIS PRINCIPIA MATHEMATICA (1687): *Mathematical Principles of Natural Philosophy* is Newton's most important work. It lays out his laws of motion and his theory of universal gravitation. This is the work that defined physics for more than two centuries, and still has a great deal to teach us today.

OPTICKS (1704): A remarkable work in which Newton describes his revolutionary experiments in light, including reflection, refraction, his complex and visionary analysis of color, and his thoughts on the behavior of prisms. The end of this volume also deals briefly with Newton's theory of atoms, which was in itself quite revolutionary at the time.

He moved to London in 1696 to take charge of the Royal Mint, and was President of the Royal Society from 1703 until his death. In 1705 he received a knighthood from Queen Anne. He died in 1727 and is buried in Westminster Abbey, London.

Optics

Newton took the study of optics to new heights. His experiments with prisms demonstrated that white light is composed of primary colors which can be separated from each other and recombined. He also reasoned (brilliantly but incorrectly) that light consists of tiny particles (which he called "corpuscles") rather than waves.

Mathematics

Newton formulated the binomial theorem of mathematics, as well as new methods for the expansion of infinite series. All of this is contained within the vast and complex branch of mathematics known as calculus. Calculus is at the heart of modern science and engineering—it has provided a platform for further discovery of how our universe works.

"Calculus" symbol

Newton is regarded as the inventor of modern calculus, but Gottfried Leibniz also has a claim.

Mechanics

Newton's three laws of motion (see pp. 46–47) and his law of gravitational attraction (pp. 48–49) became the cornerstone of all physics for the next 200 years. Newtonian mechanics (as it is still called) was the key theory of all physical interactions until the development of relativity and quantum mechanics in the twentieth century.

Newton's Laws of Motion

The formulation of the three laws of motion was perhaps Isaac Newton's greatest achievement. Even now, more than 300 years later, we are faced with their consequences every day. With every step we take, every action we perform, we see a demonstration of Newton's laws.

The First Law

> A body at rest remains at rest and a body in motion remains in motion until it is acted upon by an outside force.

Newton's first law is also called the law of inertia. Inertia is any body's tendency to resist a change in motion: it tells us how hard it is to get an object moving, as well as how hard it is to stop an object once it has started moving.

The first half of this first principle seems obvious: no one can doubt that an object will not simply start moving on its own. It is the second half of this law that is not so obvious. An object in motion will continue in motion? Doesn't that seem to go against everything we observe? If I put an object in motion, eventually it always stops. That is what the ancient Greek philosophers observed when they declared the opposite law—that every object's most natural state is that of rest, and therefore every object will eventually come to rest. What Newton realized, however, was that an object does not stop because nature wants it to stop, but because there are forces acting against it, causing it to slow down. Friction, air resistance, and physical barriers are all forces acting against every moving object on Earth. Only in the vacuum of space may we begin to see the truth of this law.

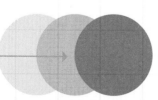

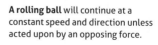

A rolling ball will continue at a constant speed and direction unless acted upon by an opposing force.

The Third Law

To every action there is always an equal and opposite reaction.

This is often called the "law of reciprocal action." Imagine two people on roller skates pushing against each other; according to Newton's third law, the two skaters will each undergo equal changes of motion, but in opposite directions. The two skaters will each be driven back by an equivalent force. We know from the second law that the acceleration of a body is directly dependent on its mass, so if the two skaters differ in mass, they will find themselves moving away from each other at different speeds.

The third law means that all forces are interactions, and thus there is no such thing as a force that operates in one direction only.

The acceleration of an object is proportional to the force acting on it and inversely proportional to the mass of the object.

The Second Law

The force applied to a body produces a proportional acceleration; the relationship between the two is $F = ma$.

In this simple equation, F represents an applied force, m represents the mass of a body, and a is the body's acceleration.

This law states that there is a relationship between the force being applied to an object and the degree to which the object accelerates, but that it is directly dependent upon the mass of the object. Therefore, it will take more force to accelerate a heavier object than a lighter object. It is much harder, for example, to push a truck down the road than it is to push a Volkswagen Beetle.

Newton's cradle demonstrates the principles of the third law as well as the idea of the conservation of energy (see p. 55).

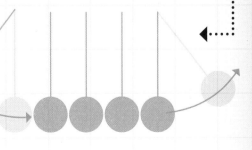

The left-hand ball decelerates from its initial speed to zero.

The right-hand ball accelerates from zero to the speed at which the left-hand ball was moving.

From Apples to Planets: Gravitation

Isaac Newton was almost certainly *not* hit on the head by a falling apple. But there does seem to have been a time when he observed the falling of an apple and began to ponder: if there is a force that draws an apple to the ground, how far does that force extend? Into the sky? Into the atmosphere? Into space? Could it be that this very same force is capable of holding the Moon in place around Earth? Newton was to prove that this is indeed the case. Everything obeys the law of gravity.

The Law of Gravitation

Here's the mathematical formulation Newton came up with:

$$F = \frac{G(m_1 \times m_2)}{r^2}$$

This equation is used to measure the force of gravitational attraction between two bodies: F refers to the force of gravity; G refers to a universally constant measure of gravitational attraction (which hadn't been precisely measured by Newton's time); m_1 is the mass of the first object; m_2 is the mass of the second object; and r is the distance between them.

Today this is known as an inverse square law—the equation defines a force which is inversely proportional to the square of the distance between two objects. In other words, as the distance increases, so the gravitational attraction will decrease at a much faster rate. As the equation shows, the most crucial factor in determining gravitational attraction is the distance between the two objects.

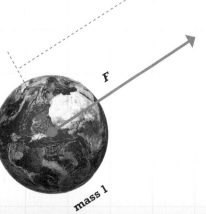

distance (r)

F

mass 1

Gravity and Particles

When we consider two bodies being gravitationally attracted to each other, we usually imagine them as completely solid bodies. In truth, Newton's law is simple only when one thinks of the most basic objects: particles. In reality, the gravitational attraction between two large objects, such as Earth and the Moon, is a massive conglomeration of gravitational attractions between the many particles that make up Earth (including you and me) and the many particles that make up the Moon. When calculating Earth's gravity in a given location, it is easy to forget that objects are not simply attracted to one particular point at the center of Earth's core. Everything is attracted to every particle that makes up the planet.

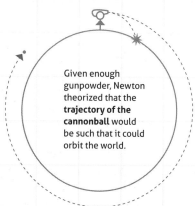

Given enough gunpowder, Newton theorized that the **trajectory of the cannonball** would be such that it could orbit the world.

Newton reasoned that if Earth is spherical (which it nearly is), then his equation works because all of these particles can be added together so the planet acts as if it had just one "center of gravity."

Into Orbit

Imagine a cannon sitting on top of a mountain, firing horizontally. Eventually, a cannonball fired from this position will fall back to Earth. By adding more gunpowder, it is possible to extend the distance it travels before being dragged down by Earth's gravity. Now, just imagine that we could put so much powder into the cannon that the ball's trajectory matched the curvature of Earth—the cannonball would not fall to the ground, but would circle all the way around the planet. It would be in orbit!

MASS AND WEIGHT: WHAT'S THE DIFFERENCE?

An object's weight is dependent on gravity, so the weight of an object on Earth will be different from the weight of the same object on the Moon. Mass, on the other hand, is entirely independent of gravity, so attempting to move an object on Earth should require precisely the same amount of energy as moving it in space. Of course, it seems more difficult on Earth, because of opposing forces such as gravity, friction, and air resistance.

Boyle's Law

Even before Isaac Newton, another branch of scientific research had already begun which would continue to be developed well into the nineteenth century—research into the nature and behavior of gases and other elements. Much of this work was performed by some of the first chemists and physicists, such as Robert Boyle and Daniel Bernoulli, whose exploration of the gaseous elements would lead to far greater understanding of chemistry, atomic theory, and even everyday mechanics.

Discovery

Before his most important work was performed in the 1660s, Robert Boyle read of a new air pump invented by Otto von Guericke, which allowed scientists to create a vacuum within an enclosed container. Boyle built one of these pumps for himself, which he then used to investigate the properties of various gases. From this research came Boyle's law, which states that for any given amount of gas at a constant temperature, its pressure and volume are inversely proportional to one another. This means that, as the volume increases, the pressure decreases by a proportional amount, and vice versa.

Do the Math

The mathematical equation for Boyle's law is:

$$pV = k$$

In this formula, p represents the pressure of a system (usually represented in units called pascals, or in atmospheres); V represents the volume of the gas (measured in cubic meters); and k represents a constant value representative of the pressure and volume of the system.

Provided the temperature is constant, Boyle's law states that the volume of a gas is inversely proportional to the pressure applied to it.

Boyle's law is arguably more important today than it was when Boyle formulated it in 1662. It lies behind air, space, and undersea travel, as well as many other applications.

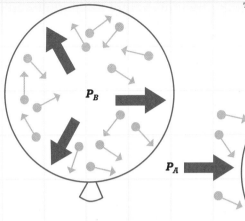

Boyle's law states that the volume of a gas is inversely proportional to the pressure applied to it.

This means that in an inflated balloon, the space that the air occupies will vary in size depending on the pressure surrounding it. On the surface of Earth, the pressure is roughly 1 atmosphere (or "atm" for short). As the pressure reaches 2 atm, the volume of the air within the balloon will shrink by half.

Boyle's Law in Action
....

When the plunger is pulled out on a syringe, the volume within the cylinder is increased, thus decreasing the pressure. Liquid (such as blood) is then drawn in to fill the partial vacuum. The human respiratory system draws air into the lungs by the same principle. Submarine designers have to allow for the effects of water pressure on the hull as the craft submerges.

THE BENDS

Though its effects were first recognized in bridge-builders working in pressurized chambers underwater, the devastating illness known as "the bends" is perhaps most well-known among scuba divers. It is a perfect (though tragic) example of Boyle's law in action.

Imagine a diver descending into the depths of the ocean, breathing pressurized air from a tank.

This air moves through the respiratory system with ease, even as the pressure around the diver increases with further descent. Now, suppose the diver reaches the ocean floor, takes a deep breath in, and then holds it in all the way back to the surface. Boyle's law predicts that as the air pressure decreases with this ascent, the gaseous nitrogen in the air will increase in volume—the air will expand! Divers are trained to avoid this terrifying prospect by never holding their breath while ascending

How Gases Move

Though the existence of atoms had been predicted by Newton and Boyle, by the eighteenth century the notion that all matter was composed of tiny, indestructible objects was still very much unconfirmed. As physicists and chemists explored the properties of gases more intently, they realized that the key to understanding the behavior of gases lay in understanding something much more fundamental: the motion of atoms.

Fluid Dynamics

In 1738 the Dutch-Swiss mathematician Daniel Bernoulli (1700–1782) published one of the first fully statistical explanations of gases. Bernoulli formulated what would eventually be called the kinetic theory of gases. He realized that he could explain the behavior of gases better by viewing them as if they were composed of large numbers of individual microscopic particles, constantly in motion and bumping into one another, bouncing here and there in completely random directions. In other words, he treated gases as if they were made of atoms.

To Bernoulli, the pressure of a gas was a measure of the number of its particles and of the speed at which they struck a given surface, such as the walls of a pressurized container. Although it is quite impossible to count these particles individually, it is possible to gauge their collective behavior statistically by using mathematical ideas well understood at that time. This analysis gave physicists a new way to explore the nature of particle motion, which led to the formulation of the laws of thermodynamics.

The pressure of a gas within a container is caused by the motion of the individual particles (molecules) within the gas.

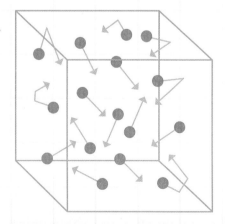

P = 100 kPa (0.987 atm)

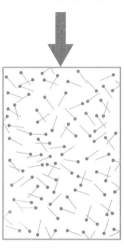

As gas is compressed into a smaller volume, so its pressure increases.

P = 200 kPa (1.97 atm)

P = 300 kPa (2.96 atm)

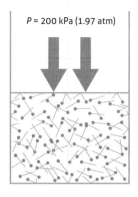

v = 6 dm³ (6 liters)   v = 3 dm³ (3 liters)   v = 2 dm³ (2 liters)

Heat into Motion

Nineteenth-century French physicist Sadi Carnot became known as the father of thermodynamics after he explained the processes at work within steam engines.

In a steam engine, water is heated to boiling point, and turns to steam. As it does so, its volume increases dramatically as a result of the increased motion of its molecules—just as Bernoulli's kinetic theory predicted. When this steam in a sealed chamber cannot expand, the pressure increases, and this pressure is used to push a piston, thus transferring heat energy (or the kinetic motion of the gas molecules) into mechanical energy, or motion.

Modern internal combustion engines use chemical energy in a similar way, making use of the combustion of certain chemicals (such as gasoline) to create the pressure necessary to drive the pistons.

Have you ever heated a pot of water until the lid starts to shake and rattle under the pressure of the steam? Then you've experienced the power of the kinetic theory of gases. As the water particles within the steam get hotter, they move faster, and the more steam is created, the more pressure all of these jostling atoms will place on the pot lid. We cannot see atoms, but we can readily see their effects.

The Laws of Thermodynamics

What is heat? What is energy? The kinetic theory of gases, which described the phenomena of heat and pressure in terms of tiny microscopic particles all jiggling around in a substance, led to a greater understanding of these questions as well. The resulting laws of thermodynamics, formulated in the nineteenth century, defined precisely how heat and energy behave and how we can use them to our advantage.

The First Law

> The increase in the internal energy of a system is equal to the amount of energy added by heating the system minus the amount lost as a result of the work being done by the system.

This law is also known as the "law of conservation of energy." Essentially, it says that the amount of energy within the universe will never change. All energy must go somewhere, and the total energy in any situation can always be accounted for.

Looking carefully at any situation will reveal the truth of this law. Imagine, for example, a car rolling down a hill and crashing into a tree. The car possesses a lot of kinetic energy (motion) as it rolls down the hill, but all of this

energy seemingly disappears as soon as it strikes the tree. Where did it go?

The energy did not disappear— it merely dispersed and changed form. The energy of motion was transformed into sound, heat, and the motion of individual particles within the vehicle that caused the structure of the car to become deformed. Many forms of energy exist, and they can all be converted into one another because energy is nothing more than motion.

Energy consists of the movement of particles and, as Newton's laws of motion clearly state, motion can be transferred from one object to another. So, although the particles in a car can transfer their motion to the particles in a tree, the motion will never disappear entirely.

The Second Law

In a system, any process will tend to increase the total entropy of the universe.

ice cube (crystal structure)

minimum entropy

maximum order

puddle of water (no structure)

maximum entropy

minimum order

Entropy is disorder, chaos. In other words, the total amount of disarray in the universe is always increasing.

In any system (a human body, a house, a planet) there is a certain amount of order. Atoms are joined with other atoms to form molecules, complex bonds create complex forms of matter, animals interact with other animals, plants grow, and so on. But this order is steadily decreasing. Consider a mirror broken into hundreds of pieces. This constitutes a decrease in order, for all those nicely aligned particles within the glass have now been fractured. Try as we might, we cannot fully restore order to this system.

CAN PERPETUAL MOTION EXIST?

The second law of thermodynamics tells us that energy is always being lost. Because of this fundamental principle, every machine requires a supply of energy in order to keep working. For hundreds of years, people have searched for a device that keeps going forever, but the principle of entropy tells us that such a device will certainly never be found. In any machine there will be energy lost, whether to friction, sound, or overcoming air resistance.

The Third Law

As temperature approaches absolute zero, the entropy of a system approaches a constant minimum.

The third law of thermodynamics was developed by William Thomson (later Lord Kelvin), several decades after the first two. Thomson recognized that, if heat is caused by the motion of particles, then there must be a point at which all heat is lost—that is, when the particles come to a complete stop. This point is absolute zero, or 0 kelvin.

The Kelvin scale was named for the work of William Thomson, 1st Baron Kelvin.

Michael Faraday

Michael Faraday perhaps best exemplifies the science of the nineteenth century. He helped to usher in a new era of science and technology— his work in chemistry led to great advances in our knowledge of matter, and his work with electricity contributed much to modern technology. He discovered electromagnetic induction and invented the electric motor.

Michael Faraday (1791–1867) began work at 13 as a book binder's assistant. His work gave him access to some of the latest scientific books, and he became passionate about physics.

Luigi Galvani (1737–98) discovered that muscles contract when an electric current is passed through them, though he was mistaken about the reason for this.

At the Royal Institution

Faraday attended lectures by the famous chemist Sir Humphry Davy, and later accompanied him on a tour of Europe, where they met many of the most prominent scientists of the day, including Ampère and Volta— two men whose names have become synonymous with electricity.

Returning to London, Faraday and Davy went back to work, with Faraday demonstrating immediately just how proficient he was at experimenting and giving lectures.

In 1821 Faraday married Sarah Barnard and in 1824 he was elected a fellow of the Royal Institution, though this promotion had actually been opposed by Davy (the society's previous president) in a fit of professional jealousy.

Three more decades of research followed, though Faraday would not live to see the culmination of his life's work and the rise of modern electronics.

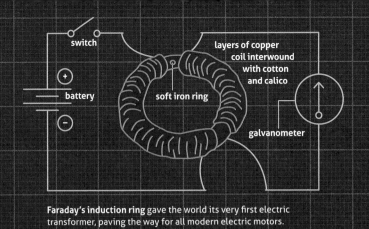

Faraday's induction ring gave the world its very first electric transformer, paving the way for all modern electric motors.

Alessandro Volta (1745–1827) was the inventor of the voltaic pile, an early form of battery which consisted of a stack of zinc and copper discs.

André-Marie Ampère (1775–1836) was a pioneer of electromagnetism, and gave his name to the SI unit of electric current, the ampere or "amp."

Faraday discovered electromagnetic rotation—a continuous circular motion caused by the circular magnetic force around a wire—and, ten years later, electromagnetic induction. His "induction ring" was the first electric transformer, and was closely followed by the first generator. By inducing motion in a magnetic field, Faraday produced an electric current and almost single-handedly ushered in the modern age of electronics.

The Work of Faraday

Faraday's most influential work centered on the relationship between electricity and magnetism. Davy had become interested in the topic and this gave Faraday the opportunity to work on it.

Though he was never known as a strong mathematician, Faraday was able to establish experimentally the direct relationship between magnetism and electricity. This would allow others after him to develop mathematical theories of light and electricity.

Faraday's research in chemistry should not be forgotten. It led to the liquefaction of chlorine and the isolation of benzene, among other things.

4

Physics in the 1800s

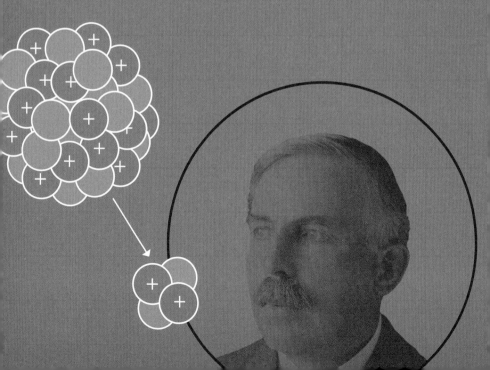

The nineteenth century was a crucial period in the development of physics. During that time the world witnessed the first theories regarding electricity, the formal discovery of the atom, and the very first attempts to delve into the subatomic realm with the discovery of the electron and of radioactivity. These breakthroughs led to tremendous practical applications as well as new physical theories. Much of what we currently know about physics has its roots in the work carried out during this century.

James Clerk Maxwell

While Michael Faraday's work laid the foundations for a fully scientific theory of electromagnetism, it was James Clerk Maxwell who first developed the mathematical theory of light and electricity. He demonstrated that even these complex concepts can be fully explained using science and mathematics.

Remarkable Intelligence

James Clerk Maxwell was born in Scotland in 1831. Educated at home to begin with, in 1841 he enrolled in the prestigious Edinburgh Academy. Though mocked by his classmates for his provincial accent and fairly humble background, he showed remarkable intelligence at this early age and developed a fascination with mathematics, especially geometry. At the age of 13 he won awards for mathematics, English, and poetry. At 14 he wrote his first mathematical paper, detailing a means of drawing mathematical curves using a piece of twine and explaining the properties of ellipses and curves with more than two foci.

Maxwell graduated from Trinity College, Cambridge, in 1854 with a degree in mathematics and went on to hold professorships in Aberdeen and London. In 1871 he became the first Cavendish Professor of Physics at Cambridge. His greatest legacy was his detailed mathematical description of electromagnetism.

In 1879, Maxwell, who had been suffering from abdominal cancer, died in Cambridge at the age of 48.

Astronomy: Maxwell theorized that Saturn's rings (first observed by Galileo in 1610) consisted of small, solid particles. This was eventually proved to be correct.

Optics: Maxwell **is credited** with the first ever color photograph, produced by projecting three monochromatic images through different-colored filters.

Boltzmann) to a mathematical model of the kinetic theory of gases. This lent greater weight to the notion that heat is a product of the motion of particles (atoms).

Maxwell also performed important mathematical work in the fields of mechanics and engineering.

His most important achievement, however, was his extension and mathematical formulation of Michael Faraday's theories of electricity and magnetism (see pp. 56–57). Maxwell showed that the behavior of both electric and magnetic fields (and the relationship between the two of them) could be expressed using only a few relatively simple mathematical equations. These equations were remarkable because they finally demonstrated mathematically that electricity and magnetism are not merely related, but they are one and the same. Maxwell showed that an oscillating electric charge produces an electromagnetic field.

Maxwell's Science

Though Maxwell is remembered today primarily for the equations he developed to explain electro-magnetism, the full range of his mathematical and scientific contributions is extensive.

His statistical explanations of moving particles (see pp. 70–71) were an essential contribution (alongside that of the Austrian Ludwig

Maxwell's equations are one of the great achievements of nineteenth-century physics. In fact, Maxwell's work on electricity and magnetism (known collectively as "electro-dynamics") is seen by many as the most important scientific advance of that period. It arguably had the greatest impact on the way people lived their lives in the twentieth century, because it enabled electricity to power the computers, vehicles, and spacecraft of the future. All users of modern technology have Maxwell to thank.

Electromagnetism: Maxwell's equations concerning electricity and magnetism (see pp.62–3) are regarded as his most important contribution to the modern world.

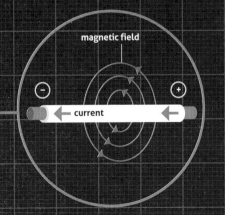

magnetic field

current

Maxwell's Equations

"From a long view of the history of mankind—
seen from, say, 10,000 years from now, there can
be little doubt that the most significant event of the
nineteenth century will be judged as Maxwell's
discovery of the laws of electrodynamics. The
American Civil War will pale into provincial
insignificance in comparison with this important
scientific event of the same decade."

—American physicist Richard Feynman

Shedding Light on Light

Prior to the work of Maxwell, light
was something of a mystery. In the
same way, before Michael Faraday's
work on electromagnetic induction,
both electricity and magnetism were
poorly understood. It was Maxwell
who saw that all of these phenomena
could be explained mathematically,
and by doing so he made the rather
astounding observation that they
could all be expressed using the
same equations.

In Maxwell's theory, light is nothing
more than a repeated oscillation
between electricity and magnetism.

"Maxwell's equations
have had a greater
impact on human history
than any ten presidents."

—Carl Sagan

Faraday had shown that electricity
and magnetism are one and the
same; light is a product of the
interaction between these two things.
Inside a ray of light one may imagine
a complex interaction between
electricity and magnetism: electricity
is produced, which creates a bit
of magnetism, which creates a bit of
electricity, and so on. According to
Maxwell, the result of this interaction
between electricity and magnetism
is not just the single ray of light but
an entire electromagnetic field.

The Equations

In 1865, Maxwell offered his theory
in the form of eight equations, each
of which explained a small piece of
the electromagnetic puzzle. Today
these equations have been reduced
to four (without changing any of their
results), as shown opposite.

electric displacement +

magnetic force +

Maxwell's equations see light as a "leapfrogging" interaction between waves of electricity and magnetism.

Faraday's Law of Induction

This is a mathematical description of Faraday's invention of the electric motor. It says that the "curl" of an electric field is dependent on the rate of change of a magnetic field. This is what Michael Faraday noticed when he was able to induce an electric charge in a loop of wire by moving a magnetic field in and out of it.

Gauss' Law for Electricity

Named after German mathematician Carl Friedrich Gauss, this first equation defines the change of an electric field (denoted as ∇). This equation is used to quantify the behavior of an electrical field in terms of its charge density in a given point of space at a given time.

$$\nabla \times E = -\partial B/\partial t$$

$$\nabla \cdot E = \rho/\varepsilon_0$$

$$\nabla \cdot H = J + \partial D/\partial t$$

$$\nabla \cdot B = 0$$

Gauss' Law for Magnetism

This one is fairly simple: it states that the overall change ($\nabla \cdot$) in a magnetic field B is always zero. In other words, magnetism is always flowing from one pole to another (such as from the positive end to the negative end of a magnet), but because the magnetism is always moving in loops, nothing is ever gained or lost. The total change is zero.

Ampère's Law

The final equation is the opposite of Faraday's law of induction. It says that a changing electric field will affect the "curl" of a magnetic field. Maxwell realized he could explain the phenomenon of light by using these two equations together. Just like that, Maxwell had explained light in all its varied forms: visible light, radio waves, gamma rays—even X-rays, which had not yet been discovered. It was now possible to deduce the speed of light.

Electricity: The Basics

Of all the scientific advancements in the nineteenth century—whether in atomic theory, chemistry, astronomy, or radioactivity—perhaps the subject which has most directly shaped the world in which we all live is the study of electricity. A large percentage of the world's population uses electricity daily—it sparked revolutions in manufacturing and in communications, and succeeded in making all our lives a bit easier. But what exactly is it?

Electricity 101

Though the existence of electricity has been known since ancient times (its name comes from the Greek word *elektron*, meaning "amber," because of that material's ability to create static electricity), it is only relatively recently that it has been understood. Today we know that electricity is simply the flow of electrons through matter.

Electrons are negatively charged particles that surround the positively charged atomic nucleus. The negative charge of an atom's electrons is usually equal to the positive charge of the nucleus. When the balance between protons and electrons is upset by an outside force, an atom may gain or lose an electron. When electrons are "lost" from an atom, the free movement of these electrons constitutes an electric current.

Some types of atoms, such as metals, allow electrons to flow through them easily (these are known as conductors); some do not allow electron flow at all (insulators); some, such as silicon, allow limited flow (semiconductors). The extent to which a material allows or prevents the flow of electricity is called the resistance of the material.

battery

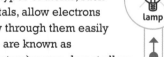
lamp

electrons   Electricity is a flow of electrons around a circuit.

Harnessing Electricity

By the middle of the eighteenth century it had already been recognized that objects could be pushed or pulled by magnetism. Electricity had been passed through wires several miles in length (which led to the telegraph, illustrated below, and all modern forms of communication), and patients were already being shocked with electricity in the hope that it might do them some good.

When Faraday demonstrated the principle of electrical induction in the middle of the nineteenth century, it was at last realized that electricity could actually be made to do real work. Faraday had shown that electricity could be created by the rotation of a magnet—a principle that was soon being used on larger and larger scales.

Today's power stations operate on precisely the principles discovered by Faraday more than a century and a half ago, using either a wind turbine, a gas-powered engine, a waterwheel, or any other machine to drive a generator that converts mechanical or chemical energy into electricity. Modern electronics uses the electrical properties of elements and transforms them into transistors, resistors, and diodes which can regulate the flow of power down to the individual electron. But no matter how complicated the technology becomes, we still depend on nothing more than the flow of electrons within atoms.

MEASURING ELECTRICITY

Four basic units are involved in measuring electricity:

- **Volts** measure the pressure of electrical current. Voltage standards differ between countries.

- **Watts** measure electric power— that is, the ability of the electricity to do work.

- **Amps** (short for **amperes**) measure the flow of the electric current— how many electrons are actually passing through the circuit.

- **Ohms** measure the resistance of a material to the flow of an electric current.

Today we can do a great many things with electricity. We can even rub our heads with balloons and make our hair stand on end.

An example of a telegraph from 1939.

Investigating Light

From the very beginning, the difficult subject of light was shrouded in mystery. Is it a substance? Is it a force? Does it move or does it simply exist? Does it travel at a finite speed? If so, just how fast is it? Though the questions were asked early on, the answers would not begin to be found until well into the Renaissance period.

The Speed of Light

In 1638, Galileo attempted to determine the speed of light by measuring the delay as a light signal flashed from one lantern to another. The experiment was a failure: light was simply too fast to be measured in this way.

Less than 40 years later, in 1676, Danish astronomer Ole Rømer made a monumental discovery as he was studying Io, one of the moons of Jupiter. Rømer recognized that Io's orbit around Jupiter was not always consistent from his perspective on Earth. He correctly deduced that this might be caused by the delay in the light traveling from Jupiter to the Earth. Rømer calculated the speed

Ole Rømer observed the orbit (C–D) of Io around Jupiter (B), relative to Earth's orbit (E–H, K–L) around the Sun (A).

of light at roughly 220,000 kilometers per second—certainly closer than anyone before had come to the presently agreed value.

Light: What Is It?

By the eighteenth century, a finite value for the speed of light had been accepted. Now attention turned on the very substance of light itself.

Newton, among others, believed that light consisted of particles (he called them "corpuscles"), while the Dutch physicist Christiaan Huygens maintained that light traveled as waves. A century later, the experimental work of Thomas Young would favor Huygens and show that light did indeed move as a wave; this theory was soon adopted by the majority of physicists.

But the details of light's substance remained yet unclear until Maxwell published his monumental theory of electromagnetism in 1864, demonstrating that light waves were nothing more than electromagnetic waves. His equations could be used to mathematically derive the speed at which these forces interact, which just so happened to precisely match the measured speed of light.

The Universal Constant

Calculations of the speed of light were further refined through the nineteenth century, eventually bringing us to the currently accepted value of 299,792.458 kilometers per second, but we also came to understand some very peculiar things about this speed.

Through the experiments of Armand Fizeau in 1851, and Albert Michelson and Edward Morley in 1887, a rather peculiar fact became clear: the speed of light was not a quantity that could be measured relative to one's own speed, but was a universal constant. This means that the speed of light is always the same, no matter how fast a person is traveling relative to the light. If one person is stationary while another is moving at 10,000 kilometers per hour, the measured speed of light will remain the same for both individuals. This realization is crucial to Einstein's theory of special relativity.

The Michelson–Morley experiment measured the speed of light in two directions, using three mirrors, one of which was partially transparent.

MICHELSON & MORLEY

In 1887, Albert Michelson and Edward Morley designed one of the most important experiments in the history of physics. Up to that time it was still believed that the universe was filled by an invisible substance called either (first theorized by Aristotle). Michelson and Morley attempted to detect the presence of either by seeing if light traveled more slowly when moving against the ether than when traveling with it. They discovered that not only did the ether not have any effect on the speed of light (leading many to believe that it didn't exist in the first place), but that the measured speed of light did not change at all relative to the motion of the Earth! The Michelson–Morley experiment eventually helped lead to Einstein's special theory of relativity (see pp. 90–91).

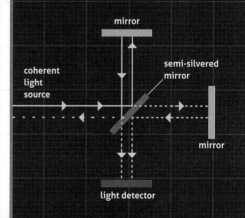

coherent light source

mirror

semi-silvered mirror

mirror

light detector

Uncuttable Things: Atoms

Although the earliest atomic theory originated more than 2,500 years ago with the Greek philosopher Democritus, this idea was effectively killed by the "elemental" theory of Empedocles, which remained dominant well into the modern era of science. In the eighteenth and nineteenth centuries, however, atomic theory staged a comeback.

The Atom Reborn

Though the existence of atoms had been speculated about for centuries, it was the English chemist John Dalton (1766–1844) who finally presented a fully workable view of atomic theory. By taking extensive measurements of the pressures and masses of many different gases, he came to the view that their properties might be dependent on the tiny particles (atoms) from which they were formed. Dalton went on to theorize that different atoms of differing weights could account for all of the various known elements.

Consequently, Dalton was the first physicist to attempt to create a table of atomic weights (a rough one in 1803, then a better one in 1805). Dalton's table would be expanded upon to near perfection by the Russian chemist Dmitri Mendeleyev more than 60 years later, resulting in a periodic table very similar to the one used today.

John Dalton also developed some of the basic principles of atomic theory, such as the fact that all atoms of a given element are identical in every way; no two elements share any common atoms; and atoms can bind together to form compounds.

Table of elements and their atomic weights, from Dalton's *New System of Chemical Philosophy*, published in 1808.

Dalton's Imperfect Theory

There was one nearly fatal flaw in John Dalton's logic regarding atomic theory, however. In his list of atomic "rules" he stated that there could be nothing smaller than an atom, despite the fact that there was not yet (nor would there ever be in the future) any real evidence that this was the case. In his mind, he had found the most basic building blocks of the universe.

Dalton turned out to be quite wrong about this, but nonetheless made great headway with the rather basic scientific tools that were available in his day. Dalton died relatively confident that his atoms did, in fact, exist, but he could not possibly have foreseen the discovery of their complex structure, their many parts, or the forces that bind them all together. He never suspected that the theory he played such an important role in forming would lead ultimately to the Large Hadron Collider—a multi-billion-dollar particle accelerator designed specifically to probe the depths of these tiny little objects.

Dalton stated that these particles must, by definition, be indivisible—as the name itself means "uncuttable" in Greek.

Why We Can't See Atoms

It is hardly surprising that it took so long for atomic theory to catch on. Atoms are, by definition, invisible.

For something to be seen by the human eye, it has to be larger than the wavelength of light, since things are seen by the light reflecting off them. Anything smaller than that is invisible. The shortest wavelength of visible light is just under 400 nm (that is, nanometers, or billionths of a meter). The largest possible atoms are more than a thousand times too small to be seen by the most powerful optical microscope in existence. And yet, these are the objects out of which all matter is made.

We now know that atoms are not nearly as simple as John Dalton implied. They are some of nature's most fascinating works of art.

Molecules of ether and alcohol, as drawn by John Dalton.

Brownian Motion

Even after the atom was discovered, the rather far-fetched concept of a universe made up of an uncountable number of tiny particles (atoms), all bound together by some unknown force to create all matter, remained rather difficult for many reputable scientists to believe. Although John Dalton's atomic theory was clever, and certainly very helpful to chemists, it had yet to be tested experimentally— until, that is, the remarkable work of the Scottish botanist Robert Brown.

Molecules on the Move

In 1827, Brown noticed that pollen grains placed into a clear liquid and viewed through a microscope tended to behave somewhat strangely, moving around almost as if they were alive, jumping and skipping randomly with no visible impetus or discoverable pattern.

This effect is known today as Brownian motion. It was soon discovered that the movement was caused not by the pollen grains being alive (as was a common explanation of the time), but by the grains being pushed around by the molecules within the water itself—in other words, they were being jostled about by molecules.

Brownian motion did much to prove the existence of tiny particles even in a seemingly smooth fluid such as water. The significance of this wouldn't become clear until nearly 80 years later, when Albert Einstein took the concept of Brownian motion to the next level.

Pollen grains moving randomly in a clear liquid.

Einstein's formula for the random walk results in the same random, chaotic motion exhibited by tiny particles pushed around by atoms within a liquid.

Einstein's Contribution

One of Einstein's four papers published during his "miracle" year of 1905 was entitled "A New Measurement of Molecular Dimensions & On the Motion of Small Particles Suspended in a Stationary Liquid." By examining Brownian motion, Einstein could calculate the number of water molecules per square inch to a surprising degree of accuracy, and provide statistical and mathematical formulas for the motion.

Einstein assumed that, as particles move about in a liquid, pressure is exerted on them by even smaller particles in every direction. Normally, there are roughly the same number of atoms on each side of the pollen grain, all pushing and bumping against each other randomly, so such movement should tend to cancel itself out most of the time. But now and then the pollen grain is pushed a bit more in one direction, so it moves that way, then later it is pushed in a different direction and moves another way.

Einstein found that although such movement is truly random and unpredictable, it does obey certain laws of probability, which he explained using a mathematical formula that became known as the "random walk." Atoms had become "visible" for the first time!

THE DRUNKARD'S WALK

Einstein's random walk formulation demonstrated that Brownian motion was indeed governed by the completely random motions of atoms within a liquid—but the applications of this random motion extend far beyond atomic physics. In fact, this same formula has been applied to a wide variety of subjects, such as:

Genetics: Defining the changes in gene pools over time.

Gambling: The probability of winning or losing is akin to a random walk.

Economics: Modeling the rise and fall of share prices.

Intoxication: The random walk can be used to model the seemingly random movements of a drunk individual attempting to find the way home from a bar. For this reason the model is often called the "drunkard's walk."

Discovering the Electron

....

The atom was discovered at the beginning of the nineteenth century. Although it would take well over a century before the scientific community at large was finally convinced of the existence of atoms, physicists had already begun to probe deeper into matter—only to discover even smaller things. The first of these "subatomic" (smaller than an atom) particles was the electron.

Thomson's Experiment

....

Credit for the discovery of the electron goes to British physicist J. J. Thomson—a man who is known not just as a great physicist (he won a Nobel Prize in 1906), but also as a phenomenal teacher, since seven of his students, and his own son, went on to win Nobel Prizes themselves.

Thomson's discovery came in 1897 while he was experimenting with a cathode ray tube—an electronic device that sends a beam of particles between a positive and a negative terminal within a vacuum tube (see "Cathode Rays," opposite).

J. J. Thomson (1856–1940) deduced the existence of the electron while experimenting with cathode rays. He observed the bending of the rays using a Crookes tube (opposite).

It was not clear at the time what cathode rays were made of, but Thomson's experiments determined that whatever it was, it possessed an electric charge—he was able to bend the ray using a magnetic field and then measure the direction of bend to determine how much mass was involved and how it was charged. Thomson found that these rays were made up of tiny particles, much smaller even than an atom (this could be determined by the amount of bending in a given magnetic field). For the first time, it had been shown that something smaller than an atom existed—in the form of tiny, negatively charged particles.

Reaction to the Electron

Many experiments were needed to prove conclusively the existence of electrons, and still no one knew what they looked like, what their function was, or why they existed at all. Many of the same questions are still being asked today.

Electrons, it is now known, are fundamental pieces of the atomic structure. They provide the necessary balance of charge in order to "neutralize" the atom, and they also form all the bonds between atoms. In other words, without electrons, molecules would never form and atoms would stay separate.

Electrons are not merely the source of electrical current (though they play that highly important role as well)—they are the reason that matter exists in the first place.

Thomson's experiment was indeed crucial, and jump-started an entire wave of subatomic discoveries, including the next step in understanding the atom: the discovery of the atomic nucleus.

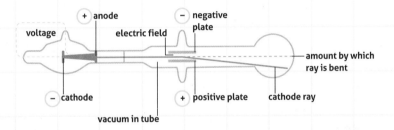

voltage

+ anode   electric field

− negative plate

− cathode

+ positive plate   cathode ray

vacuum in tube

amount by which ray is bent

CATHODE RAYS

Before the advent of modern flat-screen televisions, cathode rays were the driving force behind the creation of a picture on a television set. Rays of electrons were emitted from an electrically charged piece of metal and directed by magnets to strike one of thousands of multicolored phosphorescent dots littering the screen, causing that dot to light up. Repeat this process thousands of times every second, and you have the makings of a moving picture.

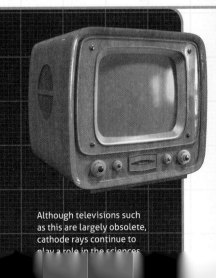

Although televisions such as this are largely obsolete, cathode rays continue to play a role in the sciences.

Ernest Rutherford

Known as the father of nuclear physics, Ernest Rutherford was responsible for an astonishing number of discoveries in the field of particle physics (a field that he himself helped to invent), including the discovery of the atomic nucleus, the proton, and the three forms of radioactive decay. He predicted the neutron, and created the modern atomic model.

The British Kiwi

A New Zealander by birth, Ernest Rutherford (1871–1937) moved to Cambridge, England, in 1895 to study with J. J. Thomson. Here he carried out his initial investigations into the new field of radioactivity.

His experiments with uranium and thorium led him to coin the terms "alpha particles" and "beta particles" for those two forms of radioactivity already known. A third, gamma radiation, would not be discovered until the work of Paul Villard in 1900.

Rutherford spent ten years at McGill University, Montreal, Canada, before moving back to England in 1907 to work at the University of Manchester. He won the 1908 Nobel Prize in Chemistry, and was knighted in 1914. Finally, in 1919 he succeeded J. J. Thomson as Cavendish Professor of Physics at Cambridge. He remained at Cambridge until his death in 1937.

> **"**All science is either physics or stamp collecting.**"**
>
> —**Ernest Rutherford**

Rutherford is one of the few individuals (alongside Albert Einstein, Enrico Fermi, and Marie Curie) to have an element named after him—the radioactive Rutherfordium.

He has had a crater on the Moon named for him.

Numerous institutions, including Rutherford College in New Zealand and Rutherford College in the UK, have been named for him.

Several institutions have named buildings in his honor.

The Gold Foil Revolution

The very next year after winning the Nobel Prize saw Rutherford and his students, Hans Geiger and Ernest Marsden, undertaking the "gold foil" experiment which led to his prediction of the atomic nucleus. Rutherford predicted that the nucleus was made up of positively charged particles (protons), which he helped to discover. He later suggested that there might be a neutrally charged counterpart to protons. The neutron was duly discovered by one of Rutherford's former students, James Chadwick, in 1932.

Not only was Rutherford primarily responsible for the creation of the first atomic model (the aptly named "solar system" model), but he was also partially responsible for the improvement on this model developed by one of the first quantum physicists, Niels Bohr, who had moved to England from Denmark in order to study with the great Rutherford. By adding quantum mechanics to Rutherford's model, these two great minds—Rutherford

one of the last great nineteenth-century thinkers and Bohr one of the first great minds of the twentieth—developed the Rutherford–Bohr atomic model, which helped to jump-start quantum mechanics, thus bringing science into an entirely new era.

The gold foil experiment enabled Rutherford to theorize the existence of the atomic nucleus. Most of the alpha particles pass through the gold foil, but a few are deflected from it (see p. 76).

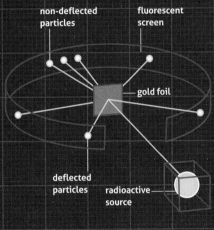

non-deflected particles

fluorescent screen

gold foil

deflected particles

radioactive source

Streets in the US, UK, and New Zealand have been named for him.

He has been the subject of a major play.

And the list goes on. . .

His image appears on the $100 bill in New Zealand.

The Subatomic Realm

The discovery of the electron by J. J. Thomson in 1897 opened up an exciting new world of possibilities, and before long it became clear that there might be other undiscovered particles lurking within the atom. Soon physicists had begun to develop theories of what an atom might actually look like, as ingenious new experiments heralded the discovery of still more pieces of the atomic puzzle.

Plum Pudding and Orbiting Electrons

The first viable atomic model was Thomson's "plum pudding" model, which paints an amusing mental picture of an atom as a "pudding" of positive matter, with little "plums" of negative electrons scattered throughout.

In 1909, Ernest Rutherford presided over a famous experiment which put the plum pudding model to the test. Alpha particles (a type of naturally occurring radiation) were fired into a very thin sheet of gold foil (see p. 75). If the plum pudding model was correct, then many of the particles passing through should have their courses slightly altered by the charge within the atoms.

But this did not happen. While most of the alpha particles passed right through the foil as if it wasn't even there, a small fraction of them were diverted at very dramatic angles as if striking a solid surface and bouncing off.

Rutherford realized that the plum pudding model could not account for this, and in 1911 he proposed a new and improved atomic model. In the Rutherford model, he posited that the negative electrons orbited around a tiny, positively charged, and incredibly dense central "nucleus," like planets orbiting a tiny sun. Though this model may not be entirely

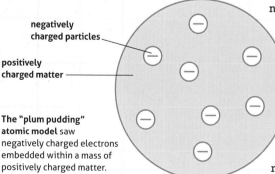

negatively charged particles

positively charged matter

The "plum pudding" atomic model saw negatively charged electrons embedded within a mass of positively charged matter.

electron

neutron

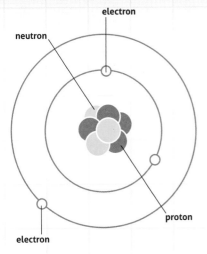

electron

proton

The "solar system" atomic model was a significant step toward today's model, with electrons orbiting a hard, dense nucleus made of both protons and neutrons.

which by itself constitutes the nucleus of a single hydrogen atom. The proton in the nucleus was recognized to be the positive counterpart to the electron, thus creating a neutral atom.

The Neutron

accurate, it has proved very useful in explaining certain fundamental features of atomic structure.

What's in a Nucleus?

What was the nucleus made of? Rutherford knew that whatever it was had to be positively charged and very dense, but this left a lot still to be explained. In 1918 he performed another experiment, bombarding nitrogen gas with alpha particles, leading to a surge of hydrogen. He correctly deduced that the hydrogen atoms must have come from within the nitrogen atoms, which meant there was something within all of these atoms which was divisible, so that a lighter element could be "removed" from a heavier element. This lighter particle was the proton,

In 1932, Rutherford's student James Chadwick discovered the neutron after performing a series of tests on a new type of radiation which had been baffling physicists for years. Chadwick bombarded a sample of beryllium with alpha particles, causing it to emit this mysterious radiation. The radiation would strike a proton-rich surface and some of the protons would be discharged. Chadwick knew that the radiation was neutral, and it had to be somewhat heavy in order to discharge something as heavy as protons. The radiation was made of neutrons.

For his achievement of completing the basic atomic model, Chadwick received the Nobel Prize in 1935.

While most of the alpha particles passed right through the gold foil as if it wasn't even there, a small fraction of them were diverted at very dramatic angles as if striking a solid surface and bouncing off.

During a lifetime, Marie Curie was a rarity—a female scientist in a field dominated by males. Despite this disadvantage, her work was brilliant. So good in fact that Curie has the rare distinction of having won not just one but two Nobel Prizes, in physics and chemistry. She, along with her husband Pierre, helped to invent the field of atomic physics—a field whose mysteries are still being discovered today.

A Winning Team

....

Born Maria Skłodowska in Warsaw, Poland, in 1867, the woman who would become Marie Curie was the daughter of a schoolteacher. Having received basic schooling from her father, in 1891 Marie went to study in Paris at the Sorbonne, where she excelled in both physics and math. Within just a few years of moving to France she had met and married physics professor Pierre Curie.

Marie and Pierre Curie formed one of the few husband-and-wife teams to have obtained prominence within the world of physics (another such Nobel Prize-winning team would consist of the Curies' daughter Irène and her husband Frédéric Joliot).

Marie Curie became interested in the recent discovery of radiation by Henri Becquerel. She began studying uranium radiation, using new and revolutionary techniques (some

While most elements possess certain isotopes that succumb to radioactive decay, those shown in blue are known to be the most radioactively unstable, having no stable isotopes at all.

H																	He
Li	Be											B	C	N	O	F	Ne
Na	Mg											Al	Si	P	S	Cl	Ar
K	Ca	Sc	Ti	V	Cr	Mn	Fe	Co	Ni	Cu	Zn	Ga	Ge	As	Se	Br	Kr
Rb	Sr	Y	Zr	Nb	Mo	Tc	Ru	Rh	Pd	Ag	Cd	In	Sn	Sb	Te	I	Xe
Cs	Ba		Hf	Ta	W	Re	Os	Ir	Pt	Au	Hg	Ti	Pb	Bi	Po	At	Rn
Fr	Ra		Rf	Db	Sq	Bh	Hs	Mt	Ds	Rg							

		La	Ce	Pr	Nd	Pm	Sm	Eu	Gd	Tb	Dy	Ho	Er	Tm	Yb	Lu
		Ac	Th	Pa	U	Np	Pu	Am	Cm	Bk	Cf	Es	Fm	Md	No	Lr

...vised by her husband), and soon Pierre had ceased his own research in order to join his wife.

By 1898 the Curies were announcing the discovery of two new elements, radium and polonium (the latter named after Marie's native Poland), and Marie became the first person to use the term "radioactive."

After Pierre's tragic and untimely death in 1906, Marie and Irène went on to promote the use of radium to alleviate suffering during World War I. Marie later established a radioactivity laboratory in her native Warsaw. The institute opened in 1932.

Unfortunately, the radioactivity to which Curie dedicated her professional life proved to be her downfall. She passed away in Savoy, France, in 1934, from pernicious anemia brought on by her exposure to excessive amounts of radiation.

Curie's Legacy

The Curies' first great achievement was in recognizing that the radiations emitted from pitchblende (a naturally occurring, uranium-rich radioactive ore) were even more intense than those from uranium itself. This led to the discovery of elements even more radioactive than uranium: radium and polonium.

Marie Curie went on to develop methods for the separation of radium in sufficient quantities to allow for a full study of its properties, including its therapeutic benefit for patients

...suffering from cancer. This became just one of the many practical uses for radioactivity.

Marie and Pierre Curie shared the Nobel Prize for physics with Henri Becquerel in 1903, for their study of radiation. Eight years later (after Pierre's death), Marie won a second Nobel Prize, this time in chemistry, in recognition of her work in radioactivity. Only four individuals have ever won the award twice.

"Nothing in life is to be feared, it is only to be understood. Now is the time to understand more, so that we may fear less."

Marie Curie

Radioactivity

Most of us have heard of radioactivity. We know that it is dangerous and probably best avoided. We know that it is left over from atom bombs and from nuclear power plants and that it is hugely controversial. But what of the science of radioactivity? The study of this phenomenon has been ongoing for more than a century, but we still have much to learn about this powerful and mysterious force in which atoms spontaneously break apart.

Early Studies

French physicist Henri Becquerel was fascinated by the subject of atomic phosphorescence (substances that emit a glow, especially after having been energized by exposure to light), and performed tests on various phosphorescent compounds.

In 1896, Becquerel noticed an odd thing when he was experimenting on potassium uranyl sulfate, a compound containing uranium. He found that the compound would "radiate" even without exposure to the Sun, leaving traces on a photographic plate nearby, even if wrapped in an opaque material.

Whatever was coming out of the compound penetrated right through various materials, just like X-rays (a form of high-frequency electro-magnetism discovered only a year previously). Whatever was causing

this radiation must be a property of the chemical compound itself. In this way, Becquerel discovered atomic radiation.

Marie Curie then showed that several different compounds were radioactive and that they all seemed to have the element uranium in common. She later found that thorium was also radioactive, and discovered two new radioactive elements, radium and polonium. Curie's work led to the understanding that only certain forms of the heaviest elements were radioactive.

Alpha, Beta, Gamma

The next great step came from Ernest Rutherford, who noticed in 1898 that radiation came in at least two different types, which he called alpha and beta, after the first letters of the Greek alphabet. Rutherford believed alpha particles to be hydrogen nuclei, though later tests

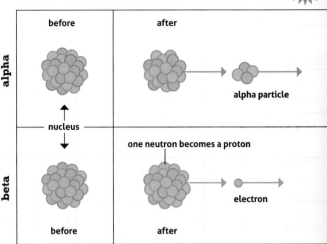

In **alpha decay**, the nucleus of the atom releases an alpha particle, which is made up of two protons and two neutrons.

neutron   proton

In **beta decay**, an electron is emitted from the atomic nucleus, turning a neutron into a proton and changing the chemical composition of the atom, such as from carbon to nitrogen.

showed that they were actually helium nuclei. Beta particles are escaping electrons.

A third type of radiation, consisting of highly energetic electromagnetism (light), was discovered in 1900 by French physicist Paul Villard and named gamma radiation. Gamma radiation has a very short wavelength, which enables it to pass through dense materials. Gamma rays are much more intense than X-rays, or even the ultraviolet light which causes the Sun's rays to burn human skin.

Spontaneous Radioactive Decay

These first nuclear physicists noticed that elements appeared to undergo radioactive "decay" for no apparent reason. Particles of radiation seemed prone to jumping randomly out of the atomic nucleus, and this was difficult either to measure or to

predict. After careful study it became clear that only certain isotopes of certain atoms, known as radionuclides, are radioactive. (An isotope is a form of an element containing the same number of protons but a different number of neutrons.) Radioactivity occurs in these isotopes because the combination of protons and neutrons makes them unstable.

Although at the time it was not clear what held the nucleus together, we are now familiar with the strong nuclear force, which provides an incredibly powerful bond between the components of the nucleus. Even with this strong force operating between protons and neutrons, however, sometimes it is only by a fine thread that the nucleus is kept stable. In the larger atoms, the force does not have enough range to keep all the particles together.

The Fall of Classical Physics

The greatest scientific advancements come not when our experiments prove theories to be ever more accurate. They come instead when the experiment no longer supports the theory and we are forced into a dramatic rethink. This is precisely what happened toward the end of the nineteenth century, when a glaring problem in early particle physics demonstrated that perhaps the laws of physics were not as well understood as most scientists had assumed.

Blackbody Radiation

By the 1890s, physicists thought they had just about everything figured out. But a few seemingly harmless questions arose. For example: how does a red-hot piece of metal fit into the world of classical physics?

A substance such as this red-hot metal is what physicists would call a "blackbody"—a material that absorbs all of the electromagnetic radiation (light) that hits it, without reflecting any of it back. Though a simple piece of metal is not a perfect blackbody, it serves as a good example.

The behavior of red-hot metal caused a crisis in physics—and a revolutionary new beginning.

Despite its name, a blackbody is not always black, and this is where the problem lies. A blackbody's color, like a black metal poker stuck into a fire, depends on its temperature. As it absorbs energy from the fire, it glows red, then orange, and finally white as its temperature increases.

This change in color occurs because as temperature increases, the wavelength of the electromagnetic radiation coming from it decreases (the heat absorbed by a blackbody is emitted in the form of heat radiation), thus changing into visible colors with shorter wavelengths. So far, so good.

Ultraviolet Catastrophe

The problem is that the laws of classical mechanics state that blackbodies which have achieved thermodynamic equilibrium (that is, are absorbing as much energy as they radiate back out) should radiate energy at every wavelength. This means that when a blackbody gets hot enough, the amount of radiation given off should approach infinity. In other words, a glowing body should in theory emit a tremendous amount of radiant energy that is strong enough to burn up everything in sight. Obviously, this doesn't happen. Either something is wrong with the blackbodies themselves (not very likely), or something is wrong with classical physics (very likely).

When the actual radiation emitted from a blackbody was measured, it did not shoot toward infinity at the ultraviolet region of the electromagnetic scale (as the theories suggested), but reached its peak toward the middle of the visible range of the spectrum, which seemed entirely illogical. The discrepancy became known as the "ultraviolet catastrophe."

Planck's Solution

It was Max Planck who finally provided a mathematical solution to this problem. His deceptively simple equation is called Planck's law of blackbody radiation:

$$E = h\nu$$

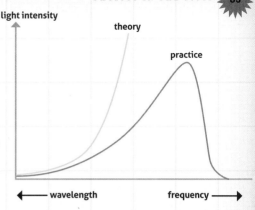

light intensity

theory

practice

wavelength ← — → frequency

The Ultraviolet Catastrophe occurs where practice diverges from theory: in classical physics light should be emitted from blackbodies with infinite intensity, while practical experience shows otherwise.

E represents the thermal radiation produced by a blackbody; ν (which is actually the Greek letter "nu") is the frequency of the electromagnetism being released; and h is a new constant, dubbed Planck's constant (which has a very tiny estimated value of somewhere very close to 6.626068×10^{-34} J•s). And that's it— a fairly simple equation that solved one of the biggest questions facing the scientific world at the end of the nineteenth century.

What Does It Mean?

Planck's constant represents the smallest possible unit of radiation, which eventually became known as a photon—a particle of light. Throughout the nineteenth century it had been shown that light traveled as waves. Planck's theory implied that, within these waves, light did in fact exist as particles after all! Planck had "quantized" light; quantum physics was born.

5.

The Birth of a New Physics

The study of physics was turned upside
down at the beginning of the twentieth
century by the discovery of two different
but equally revolutionary fields of science:
relativity and quantum mechanics.
This chapter offers a brief introduction to
each of these exciting branches of physics and
demonstrates just how important they have
been to the continued pursuit of science.

Max Planck

December 14, 1900, may be considered the birthday of quantum physics, although even those present that day—remarkably intelligent scientists who surely understood every word of it—seem to have come away wholly unimpressed. It seems the significance of what they had witnessed was not immediately evident to them. On the day in question, Max Planck presented a paper to the German Physical Society that offered a solution to the problem of blackbody radiation. The simple formula contained within Planck's paper would transform the world of physics.

Planck's Life

Max Planck was born in Kiel, Germany, in 1858. His father was a law professor. The family moved to Munich in 1867, where Max was enrolled in a local school and began to learn the basic principles of mathematics, astronomy, and mechanics. Though he was gifted in a number of areas (he was a talented musician), Planck chose to study physics at the University of Munich and later at the University of Berlin. At the former, Planck received much of his formal training in physics; at the latter, he studied under the physicist Hermann von Helmholtz

and became interested in the field of heat theory. This would be his primary area of study throughout the latter decades of the nineteenth century.

Planck's Greatest Achievement

When Planck finally did offer up a potential mathematical solution to the blackbody problem, its non-classical nature was rather unexpected, but not entirely groundbreaking. The physics community was quite simply unsure what to make of it—a theory that seemed to work just fine on paper, but which seemed to neglect certain physical "truths" which had previously been taken for granted. It failed to adhere to the set of classical formulas which governed the whole of physics at the time. So, what had Planck discovered, and why was it so difficult to digest?

light as a particle

light as a wave

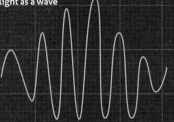

Max Planck scarcely believed the consequences of his own research: that light could behave as both a wave and a particle.

Planck's equation described the blackbody phenomena in a purely mathematical sense, but he did not provide any physical explanation. It was therefore not immediately clear what Planck's work signified. While figuring out how best to calculate the seemingly discontinuous nature of a very specific form of light, Planck had not yet even begun to explain what was happening within a blackbody that might cause it to emit radiation as it did. When he did try to explain it, he was only partly correct.

> **"**Scientific discovery and scientific knowledge have been achieved only by those who have gone in pursuit of it without any practical purpose whatsoever in view.**"**
>
> —**Max Planck**

The Incredulity of Planck

It would take five more years and the work of a young and almost completely unknown patent clerk named Albert Einstein (see pp. 88–89) for Planck's theories to gain any traction. When Einstein looked at Planck's equation, applying it to another problem that had cropped up in the previous decade, his conclusion stated what Planck's equation had only implied: light behaves as a wave, but is at the same time broken up into particles, which were later referred to as photons.

Though Planck never fully accepted the quantum physics that he helped to invent, he was nevertheless awarded a Nobel Prize in Physics for his efforts in 1921. He lived until 1947.

Max Planck's legacy is assured through the work of his 13 eponymous centers (shown here in yellow) and two partner institutes (in orange).

Albert Einstein

Albert Einstein's two great theories of relativity (which he called the "special" and the "general" theories) form one of the great branches of twentieth-century science, and help bridge the gap between classical and modern physics. They are the theories by which a virtually unknown German researcher sought to supplant Isaac Newton as history's most influential physicist.

Young Einstein

Albert Einstein was born into a Jewish family in Ulm, Germany, in 1879. Although gifted, he did not immediately excel at school.

As a teenager he became fascinated by mathematics (specifically geometry) and began to ponder such abstract questions as what it might be like to be able to travel at the speed of light. His own work would eventually provide some real answers to this question.

Einstein's Politics

Throughout much of his life, Einstein was nearly as active in politics as in science. In order to stay out of the armed services he renounced his German citizenship at the age of 17, quitting school and moving with his family to Italy. After enrolling at the Federal Institute of Technology in Zürich, he became a citizen of Switzerland. He returned to Germany, where he taught for several years at the University of Berlin, before moving to the United States in 1933, partly in response to the rise of Fascism in Europe.

Einstein had long been a champion of peace, though in the midst of World War II he famously wrote to President Roosevelt urging him to move forward in building a nuclear weapon, for fear that the Germans might do so first. This was the extent of Einstein's involvement with nuclear weapons, but it was enough to cause him considerable guilt after they had been used against Japan.

Einstein lived in Princeton, New Jersey (where he taught at the Institute for Advanced Studies) until his death in 1955, just a few years after turning down an offer to become president of the new nation of Israel.

"The most incomprehensible thing about the world is that it is comprehensible."

—**Albert Einstein**

Scientific Achievements

Besides his two theories of relativity, Einstein did outstanding work in quantum mechanics (for which he won the 1921 Nobel Prize), atomic theory, and cosmology.

The year 1905 is commonly referred to as Einstein's *annus mirabilis*—his "wonderful year." Over the course of 12 months, Einstein—totally unknown in the scientific world up to that point—published a total of five papers. Two of these were on atomic theory, and served to demonstrate once and for all the existence of atoms and to provide means of measuring their size. Another was one of the first important papers on quantum theory. The other two papers laid the foundations of the special theory of relativity. Any one of these papers would have been revolutionary; the five of them taken together seem truly miraculous.

During the final decades of his life, Einstein's work centered on the debate over quantum mechanics and attempts to use the general theory of relativity to understand the size, shape, and behavior of the universe itself. Einstein hoped that it would lead him to a "theory of everything," which would explain all that there was to know in physics. Of course, this goal has yet to be reached.

Einstein's concepts, such as space-time (top) and special relativity (bottom), have inspired countless other ideas, including that of wormholes (middle).

$$= 1 + \tfrac{1}{2}(\tfrac{v}{c})$$
$$= 1 + \tfrac{v^2}{2c^2} + \cdots$$
$$m_m = m_r \left(1 + \tfrac{v^2}{2c^2} \right)$$
$$= m_r + m_r \tfrac{v^2}{2c^2}$$
$$m = m_r \tfrac{v^2}{2c^2}$$
$$= \dfrac{\left(\tfrac{1}{2} m_r v^2 \right)}{c^2}$$
$$m = \tfrac{e}{c^2} \qquad e = mc^2$$

Special Relativity

Albert Einstein tore up the rule book when he published his theory of special relativity. This young and unknown man suddenly told the world that everything they thought they knew about light, motion, speed, and even time was false. Though it would be years before his magnificent theory was fully accepted by other physicists, special relativity would forever change the study of physics and our perceptions of reality.

Foundations

The special theory of relativity is built upon two foundations:

Galilean Relativity
Galileo (see pp. 34–35) had offered a simple principle 300 years earlier: there can be no "preferred" frame of reference. In other words, the laws of physics within a moving vehicle (such as a boat, train, or spacecraft) are no different from the laws of physics on solid ground.

The Constant Speed of Light
Nineteenth-century physicists showed that the speed of light is constant, no matter how fast an observer is moving. Einstein discovered that Galilean relativity holds true only *because* of the constant speed of light. The laws of physics hold true in any reference frame, moving or stationary, because the speed of light will not change relative to one's motion.

The Train Analogy

Inside a moving train, a ball is dropped to the floor. To an observer on board the train, the ball will be seen to go straight down. But to an observer outside the train (if they could see through the wall of the car), the ball would appear to fall along a curved path in the direction the train is moving.

The question is: Which of these two viewpoints (the observer on the train or the observer on land) is correct (or as Einstein said, which is "preferred")?

Direction of train's movement

Ball is dropped.

When the observer is on the train, the ball appears to drop in a straight line.

In the parlance of relativity, these two different perspectives are equal and are referred to as "reference frames" or "inertial frames." All reference frames are equal, though their relative motion alters the way they are seen by outside observers. This idea of the equality of inertial frames is the key to understanding Einstein's theory of special relativity.

> In special relativity, time can slow down and speed up, objects expand and contract, and nothing is what it seems. Everything is dependent on motion.

The Constant Speed of Light

Now, we must add to the concept of relativity the idea of the constant speed of light. Imagine that you and two of your friends are racing through space using jet packs. You are all traveling at different speeds, one at 30 km/h, one at 300 km/h, and one at 3,000 km/h.

As the three of you are racing along at your various speeds, a ray of light suddenly comes zooming past you, in the same direction, at the speed of light. If all three of you were somehow able to measure the speed

of this light in relation to your own speeds, what do you suppose you would find? According to traditional methods, you would surely expect that in order to find the speed of light relative to yourself, you would simply take the speed of light (c), and subtract from it your own speed, right? Not so, if the speed of light is a constant. All three of you would continue to measure the speed of this light to be exactly the same: 300,000 km/s.

What Einstein's theory does is to combine the "basic" theory of relativity with this constant speed of light. It says that Galileo's theory of relativity does not merely relate to motion, but to the speed of light itself, and if light is a constant, everything else is relative, including even perceptions of time and space. In special relativity, time can slow down and speed up, objects expand and contract, and nothing is what it seems. Everything is relative and dependent on motion.

The path of the falling ball is seen differently, depending on whether the observer is on board the train, or looking into it from outside.

When the observer is off the train, the ball appears to drop in a curved line.

$E = mc^2$

It is surely the most famous equation in physics, yet when Albert Einstein first developed his theory of the equivalence of mass and energy, it was little more than a footnote to his theory of special relativity. It appeared in the shortest of the five brilliant papers he would publish in 1905, entitled "Does the Inertia of a Body Depend Upon its Energy Content?" In the space of just a couple of pages, Einstein laid out the blueprint for the formula which would pave the way for nuclear power, high-energy particle physics, and nearly everything we now understand about matter and energy.

Mass and Energy

In physics, mass is a measurement of an object's resistance to movement. The mass of an object determines how hard it is to move (this is called inertia), and its behavior within a gravitational field. Weight is a measure of gravity acting upon an object's mass.

Energy, on the other hand, seems on the surface like an entirely different animal. Where mass is something real and tangible, energy is more of an idea. It is often defined as "the ability to do work," and while this may leave things a bit vague, it really is rather accurate.

So, when the title of Einstein's paper asks the question, "Does the Inertia (Mass) of a Body Depend Upon its Energy Content?", he is asking, essentially, if there is a connection to be made between mass and energy.

Einstein's Equations

How are mass and energy connected to one another? First, they both obey the principle of conservation, meaning that they can be neither created nor destroyed. Though they can be converted into different forms (mass can turn from solid to liquid to gas, while kinetic energy can be transferred to potential, sound, or heat energy), there will always be the same amount in our universe. They are also related, Einstein found, in another, much more fundamental way.

Einstein began, it is said, by looking at the equation for finding an object's kinetic energy:

$E = \frac{1}{2}mv^2$

This equation, which had been around for some time, clearly shows that there is some relationship

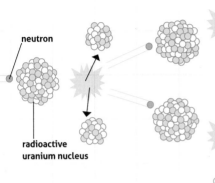

In a nuclear chain reaction, the atomic nucleus is split, releasing energy and more neutrons, which split other atoms, releasing yet more energy and neutrons.

neutron

radioactive uranium nucleus

between mass (*m*) and energy (*E*), and that their relationship is defined by the velocity (*v*) of an object.

Einstein was able to combine this with other known equations, do a little bit of math, and come up with the following:

$$E = mc^2/\sqrt{(1-v^2/c^2)}$$

This, in essence, is the equation Einstein published in his paper. The equation most people are familiar with, $E = mc^2$, can be obtained by assuming that the object in question has a speed (velocity) of zero:

$$E = mc^2/\sqrt{(1-0)}$$

$$E = mc^2$$

Same Thing, Different Packaging
••••••••••••••••••••••••••

This equation shows that mass and energy are not just similar—they are the same thing, but in different forms.

Mass can be turned into energy, and energy into mass. Furthermore, the equation shows that a tiny bit of mass can be turned into a lot of energy (the equivalent of the amount of mass times the speed of light squared), while a lot of energy can only be turned into a little bit of mass. $E = mc^2$ still drives experimental and theoretical physics today.

It would eventually be possible, using radioactive elements, to actually turn regular matter into pure, intense energy. The result was the atomic bomb, and later atomic energy. But perhaps even more interesting is the notion that all matter—you, me, a rock, a chair— is composed of pure, intense energy. You and I are like living, breathing nuclear reactors!

General Relativity

Einstein's theory of special relativity was "special" because it was concerned only with certain very specific situations, where objects travel in perfectly straight paths and at constant speeds. For a full decade following his work in 1905, Einstein sought to expand his theory to include not just these special circumstances but *all* objects. The result was his theory of general relativity, which gave the world an entirely new definition of gravity.

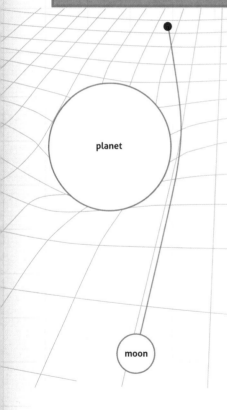

A planet in space creates gravity by curving space-time around itself, causing the path of its moon to bend; this is the first step in explaining orbits.

A Happy Thought

In 1907, Einstein had what he called "the happiest thought of my life." He imagined that a person accelerating through space in a ship would feel the force of the acceleration pushing against them. This would feel exactly the same as the sensation of being pulled down to the ground by gravity on Earth. In other words, it is impossible to tell the difference between motion and gravity. This concept became known as the principle of equivalence.

Over the next ten years Einstein would expand upon this principle to determine that gravity must be caused, in one way or another, by acceleration—as if we are constantly "falling" into the surface of the Earth!

Warped Space

Using a branch of mathematics called non-Euclidean geometry, Einstein formulated a theory in which neither space nor time is flat. Instead, both space and time are warped by the presence of mass, which causes them to curve.

A good way to think about this is to picture a bowling ball on a trampoline. As the ball sits on the flexible surface, it creates an indentation. In general relativity, the same thing happens when a massive object (like Earth, the Moon, or the Sun) sits in the "fabric" of space-time. Space and time must both "curve" around it, and it creates an indentation in the very dimensions of the universe. The more massive the object, the larger the indentation and the greater the area influenced by the object's presence.

If a smaller ball is rolled toward the bowling ball, its path will be altered by the indentation created by the larger ball. This is the principle by which the Moon orbits Earth.

Straight Lines Through Curved Space-Time
....

One surprising element of general relativity is that objects do not actually curve when they are caught up in a gravitational field. An object like the Moon appears to be traveling in a circular orbit but is actually following a straight path. It is not the path of the moon that bends, but space-time itself! This is not as strange as it seems. After all, we live on the curved surface of Earth. The shortest distance between two points is not a straight line, but one that follows the curvature of

Earth. The shortest distance between two points in curved space is known as a "geodesic." In Einstein's theory, all motion in the universe must be calculated using a new geometry which describes the curvature of space-time and an object's geodesic path through this curvature.

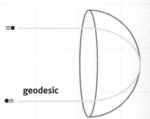

Geodesics describe the motion of particles (here following the yellow path) along the curvature of space-time.

geodesic

SPACE, TIME, AND GRAVITY

Just as in special relativity, in general relativity we must deal with the "flexible" nature of both space and time. Where in special relativity the speed of an object was able to alter the perception of distances and the passage of time, the same holds true for gravitation in general relativity. It was predicted by Einstein (and has been shown by experiment) that the influence of gravitation causes time and space dilation (stretching) effects identical to those caused by motion in special relativity.

The two theories are really not all that different—they both deal with motion and with space-time, but in slightly different contexts.

The Uses of Relativity

The general theory of relativity is widely regarded as Einstein's greatest accomplishment in the field of physics. With his theory of curved space-time, Einstein had rewritten the book on gravity, overturning Newton's greatest discovery, and had given the world the tools with which to use these principles in the form of some fairly complex mathematics. Now, all that was left to do was to demonstrate the validity of his theory and then use it to learn more about the universe.

Testing Relativity

Einstein came up with several ways by which experimental physicists could attempt to verify his radical new theory.

The first and perhaps most famous of these tests is that of gravity's ability to bend light. According to Einstein's theory of curved space-time, rays of light should have their paths slightly altered when passing near a massive object (and, obviously, the more massive the object, the more dramatic this alteration).

In 1919, Arthur Eddington successfully observed the light of stars passing by the Sun during an eclipse, which supported Einstein's theory. A second test of the theory concerned irregularities in the orbit of the planet Mercury, which had been

puzzling astronomers for centuries. Newton's equation wasn't able to account for the dramatic curvature of space-time which occurred near the Sun. After applying his own equations to the problem, Einstein realized that general relativity presented a neat solution to this puzzle: Mercury was the only planet close enough to the Sun to be visibly affected by the curvature.

General relativity, therefore, was not only able to explain phenomena that were already known, but could also solve previously unexplained occurrences in science.

star

Sun

When passing through the curved space-time around a star, the path of a light ray is bent, proving that gravity has an effect on light.

Earth

The Expanding Universe

In the decades following his creation of general relativity, Einstein spent much of his time trying to use it to understand the behavior of the universe. He was not immediately successful, as he was convinced that the universe was neither expanding nor contracting. When it became clear that the universe was expanding, Einstein called this "the greatest blunder of my life."

Since then, general relativity has afforded scientists an entirely new way of looking at the universe, and given rise to entire branches of science that would have made no sense without the theory.

Relativity and GPS

One result of general relativity which truly does play a role in everyday life is the creation of the Global Positioning System, a network of satellites which continually orbit the Earth and tell us precisely where we are on the planet at any given moment. It wouldn't have been possible but for our understanding of general (and special) relativity, which allows us to precisely sync the time and position of all these satellites. Without it, the effects of warped space-time on time and distance would throw out the entire system.

WORMHOLES

Some physicists have come to the conclusion that the curved nature of space-time might actually make it possible in the future to do things that are now relegated to science fiction. If space-time were to curve dramatically enough for two distant points to come close together (imagine bending a piece of paper so that the two ends almost touch), it might be possible to find a "wormhole" from one point to another distant point. This would potentially allow us to travel instantaneously from one part of the universe to another, and even to travel in time. Don't hold your breath, though—this idea still only exists in the minds of particularly creative physicists.

A

normal route (green)

wormhole route (red)

B

Quantum Revolution

The family of theories known as quantum
mechanics has become truly fundamental to
almost every branch of physics today. These
theories deal with elements of the natural world
which (but for a few exceptions) are far too
small ever to be seen, even with the fanciest
microscopes. Theories have been developed to
describe the behavior of the smallest particles
known to man, and have done so with a very
surprising degree of accuracy.

Why the Theory Matters

Very nearly all of modern physics,
theoretical and practical, is founded
on ideas that began in the first
decades of the twentieth century
with the earliest quantum physicists—
hugely important thinkers such as
Max Planck, Niels Bohr, Werner
Heisenberg, Paul Dirac, Louis de
Broglie, and Erwin Schrödinger.

What has been gained from such
studies? What is now known about
the universe? How well can we
predict the movements and

interactions of particles? Oddly
enough, it can be said with some
degree of accuracy that the advent
of quantum physics has led to a
lesser ability to predict motions and
interactions. Quantum mechanics
does not deal with the behavior of
individual particles, but focuses on
probability and statistics. In quantum
mechanics we can only ask what a
particle (or group of particles) is
likely to do, and calculate as
precisely as possible the probability
that they will behave in this way.

Quantum physics tells us that within
all things there is an inherent
"unknowability" that can never be
overcome. Yet these theories have
led us to the deepest understanding
of the physical universe that we
have yet achieved.

"Those who are not
shocked when they first
come across quantum
theory cannot possibly
have understood it."

—Niels Bohr

Basic Principles

Quantum mechanics, though complex, rests on a few key concepts:

Quantization

When something is broken up into finite, discrete quantities (such as photons of light, or individual particles such as electrons or protons), it is said to be "quantized." In quantum mechanics everything, even forces themselves, is best understood as a set of interactions between individual particles.

Wave–Particle Duality

Isaac Newton theorized that light consisted of particles. In the nineteenth century Thomas Young overturned this theory with his belief that light consisted of waves. With the onset of quantum mechanics and the work of Max Planck, it became clear that light consists, oddly enough, of both. Two decades later, physicists would begin to realize that all particles behave in a "wavelike" manner. According to quantum mechanics, however, these waves are not actual physical waves, but waves of probability, defining the chances of finding each individual quantum (photon) at any given moment. This is known as wave–particle duality.

The Heisenberg Uncertainty Principle

This defines the notion that a quantum particle can never be observed as both a particle and a wave at the same time. In other words, the wave qualities (which define the particle's momentum) and the particle qualities (which define its exact position) can never be known at the same time. One can measure either a particle's position or its momentum, but never both. Thus, a quantum particle can never be fully defined—hence the uncertainty.

Quantum mechanics remains a difficult subject even for physicists. The notion that there are limits to what we can know about the material world is only the beginning of the philosophical and metaphysical difficulties which have led such prominent physicists as Max Planck and Albert Einstein (two of the founders of these theories) to recoil in disbelief.

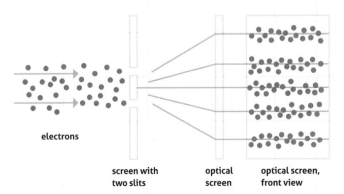

electrons

screen with two slits

optical screen

optical screen, front view

Wave–particle duality is perhaps best demonstrated in the "double slit" experiment, where individual photons of light are passed between two slits and yet interfere with each other as if they were waves.

6

Quantum Mechanics

Quantum physics has provided a foundation for some of the most important discoveries in the history of science. Although now more than a century old, it continues to dominate the thoughts of physicists. In this chapter, we look at concepts such as Heisenberg's uncertainty principle, antimatter, and the seemingly paradoxical quantum mechanics, as well as the ways in which these theories have been put to practical use.

Niels Bohr

Niels Bohr became a legend in his native Denmark—one of their most important exports, and their most intriguing character since Hamlet. The height of his worldwide fame and success came in the 1920s and '30s with his grand elucidation of the mysterious world of quantum mechanics, and his equally grand public persona— but that was well after the world had begun to accept the truth of a non-classical universe.

Part of a silicon dioxide molecule according to the Bohr model, showing one atom of silicon bonded to two of oxygen.

Philosophy and Physics

Bohr was born in Copenhagen in 1885. His father, Christian, was professor of physiology at the University of Copenhagen (he had a medical phenomenon, the Bohr effect, named after him) and his younger brother, Harald, was a mathematician.

In 1903 Bohr enrolled at Copenhagen University, initially studying philosophy and mathematics. After conducting a prize-winning series of experiments to examine the properties of surface tension, he felt encouraged to take up physics instead. In 1911 he received his doctorate and moved on to do research in England, first under J. J. Thomson at Trinity College, Cambridge, and then under Ernest

Rutherford at Manchester. It was under Rutherford's guidance that Bohr published his quantum model of atomic structure in 1913.

Bohr married Margrethe Nørlund and they had six sons, one of whom would himself win the Nobel Prize for physics in 1975. During the 1920s Bohr became one of the world's leading spokesmen for the new quantum theories. He defended these ideas against the likes of Erwin Schrödinger and Albert Einstein, thus furthering the scientific dialogue and encouraging others to question and to learn.

Bohr won the Nobel Prize in 1922 for his work in developing the new atomic model. During World War II he assisted American scientists with the atomic bomb project. He passed away in Copenhagen in 1962.

First of a New Generation

Niels Bohr's most important scientific work began with his collaboration with Ernest Rutherford at Manchester. Studying under the inventor of the modern atomic model gave Bohr a unique insight into the world of subatomic physics. He was one of the first of the "quantum generation," who had not been born when the electron was first discovered.

Bohr was the first to apply quantum mechanics to the atomic model, theorizing that as electrons orbit the atomic nucleus they are confined to specific energy levels which are defined by their absorbing and emitting quanta of light (photons). Later, by encouraging the younger generation of physicists to pursue the principles of quantum

> "We must be clear that when it comes to atoms, language can be used only as in poetry."
>
> —Niels Bohr

mechanics, he played an essential role in guiding Heisenberg toward his famous uncertainty principle. In honor of Bohr's work in formalizing the principles of quantum mechanics, the most widely held interpretation of the theory was named the Copenhagen Interpretation, after his birthplace.

Perhaps more than any other physicist in the early twentieth century, Niels Bohr embodied the science that would become known as quantum mechanics, for he had the courage to explore this strange new world with all its paradoxes.

THE BOHR–EINSTEIN DEBATES

Throughout much of the 1920s, '30s, and '40s, Niels Bohr participated in one of the great scientific rivalries in modern history. When Albert Einstein expressed his disagreement with the probability-driven quantum physics of which Bohr was a founding father, several decades of friendly debate ensued. Einstein famously developed a series of thought experiments with which he hoped to question the principles on which quantum physics was based. Rather than weakening the theory, however, Einstein's questions drove Bohr and other quantum physicists to further clarify and strengthen their ideas—which is the true purpose of scientific debate.

Niels Bohr and Albert Einstein, photographed around 1925.

The Quantum Atom

By now Ernest Rutherford had done a great deal to finally put the pieces of the atom together, deducing that these tiny chunks of matter consist of a positively charged nucleus orbited by negatively charged electrons. But physicists were still left with several important questions to answer. It would take the combined work of Rutherford and Bohr, working with a brand-new set of tools called quantum physics, to finally begin to solve these problems and create a new and improved model of the atom.

The Energy Problem

What exactly were the issues that arose as a result of Rutherford's simple "solar system" model of the atom? Perhaps the most serious was the problem of an electron's energy, and the fact that under the laws of physics as they were then understood, atoms should have been positively unsustainable.

It was already clear that electrons orbiting the atomic nucleus made use of different energy levels, and that in order to change energy levels they needed to either absorb or emit light (photons). When a photon strikes an electron, the electron absorbs the light and becomes more energetic, jumping to a higher energy level around the atom (these levels are often referred to as energy "shells"). Very quickly, however, an electron will spit that energy back out, falling back into a lower energy level.

The problem with this is that the electron, being drawn toward the positively charged nucleus, would be drawn toward the state requiring the least amount of energy, so it should continue to emit energy, falling into smaller and smaller orbits around the nucleus until these two bodies collided. All of this would happen quickly. In other words, this atomic model was highly unstable.

Bohr's Solution

The quest to find a stable atomic model led Niels Bohr to his first great contribution to atomic theory: he argued that this question of atomic stability might be solved simply by applying the already widely accepted Planck–Einstein quantum ideas to the behavior of electrons.

Einstein had shown that light exists only in quantized form (that is, as separate particles), and this idea clearly had relevance to the atomic structure. If electrons are known to both absorb and emit light, then they can only do so by way of these individual photons, in very specific, quantized amounts. An atom could not emit a partial photon, for such things do not exist.

The principle can be summed up rather simply: as the energy being emitted by an electron can only come in specific amounts—determined by the frequency of the light emitted, which is unique to each atom—an electron's orbit can only exist at very specific distances from the atomic nucleus. The precise sizes (energies) of these orbits differ with each element because the attractive or repulsive forces vary with the size of the nucleus.

The absorption and emission of light by electrons may only change the electron's orbit by exactly the amount of energy contained within a single photon. Using data gained by experiments on hydrogen atoms, Bohr found that this change

did indeed correspond precisely to the amount of energy denoted by Planck's constant—the number which defines the size of a photon of light (see p. 83). The orbits of electrons were determined by the energy carried by photons, and were thus subject directly to quantum rules.

Bohr explained why it was that electrons never collide with the atomic nucleus: they may only travel at specific energy levels, and once they reach their lowest possible energy level (their ground state) they can go no lower—except by emitting a "partial" photon, which is a quantum impossibility. A new model of the atom had been successfully created!

$n = 3$

$n = 2$

$n = 1$

increasing energy of electron orbits

Bohr's atomic model explained that electrons may only orbit the nucleus in very specific "shells," moving from one to another by absorbing or emitting photons of energy.

photon is emitted as electron jumps to a lower orbit

sunlight shines on the tomato

photons emitted by atoms of tomato's skin

When light strikes an object, the atoms in that object absorb energy and move to a higher level. When they fall back again, they emit photons. Each type of atom absorbs and emits light of specific wave-lengths, and the wavelength of the emitted light is what we perceive as the color of the object.

Explaining Electrons

Although Niels Bohr had successfully solved the most pressing issue of the atomic structure by applying the principles of quantum physics, other questions would still continue to crop up over the following decade which demanded answers. Fortunately, the answers would arrive almost as quickly as the questions could be asked, and physicists were thus led to an even greater understanding of atoms and the subatomic particles of which they are composed.

Electron Spin

By the 1920s, "quantum numbers" were being used to explain the behavior of electrons. These were three variables which defined aspects of an electron's orbit within an atom. Any given electron, it was thought, could be fully explained simply by providing a value for each of these variables.

Furthermore, by knowing the precise set of numbers for the valence (outermost) electrons of a given element, all of its chemical characteristics could be determined. However, it was soon realized that defining an

electron using just three numbers simply didn't explain everything. The only way to solve this problem was to find a fourth quantum number. This number, first described by the physicist Ralph Kronig in 1924, was given the playful name "spin." We know now that all electrons (and other particles) possess spin in one of two varieties—spin up and spin down.

The spin of an electron is a measurement of the particle's intrinsic angular momentum—

Electrons are seen to "spin" in one of two directions: up or down.

a quality which belongs to the electron itself, and which is terribly difficult to explain as there really is no analogy which fully does it justice. We simply know that it exists and without it we would have no hope of fully understanding electrons.

Level 1

Level 1

Level 2
Level 1

Level 2
Level 1

Each level or "shell" of an atom can contain only a limited number of electrons. It is the electrons in the outermost shell that determine the chemical properties of an element.

electron

nucleus

The Exclusion Principle

With this addition to the list of quantum numbers, physicists could begin to find an answer to a question which had been asked since 1913: what defines the number of electrons in each energy level of an atom? Why can each orbital hold only a certain number of electrons and no more?

In 1914 English physicist Henry Moseley used a spectroscope (an instrument which measures the distribution of color emitted by electrons) to measure electron configurations within atoms, and recognized that electrons arrange themselves only in very particular and predictable configurations, unique to each element.

Bohr's model of the atom led to these crucial insights and provided the first steps toward understanding the behavior of electrons within the confines of an atom, but at the same time it did very little to further understanding of why electrons configured themselves as they did.

The answer finally arrived with the important work of Austrian physicist Wolfgang Pauli in 1925. Pauli's exclusion principle can be stated plainly enough: no two

particles may ever be allowed to occupy the same quantum state at the same time.

When applied to electrons, this means that no two particles within an atom may ever share identical quantum numbers. If there are two electrons at the same energy level within an atom, they may have different orbital shapes, or different directions of angular velocity. If all these features are the same, then the two electrons must differ in their spin number.

It is now a generally accepted truth in physics that different energy levels within an atom may hold very specific numbers of electrons as a direct result of these atomic numbers. The exclusion principle is a fundamental property of subatomic particles—one which finally gives a full explanation of why the periodic table works as it does and why some chemicals specifically combine with others. Much of modern chemistry depends on quantum numbers.

Wave–Particle Duality

In the earliest quantum theories, light could best be seen as individual particles. At the same time, these particles clearly exhibited the behaviors of waves within the confines of certain experiments. Depending on the experiment, either of these very different forms could be seen as being valid, so which is it? As hard as it may be to believe, in the 1920s it began to be clear that something can be both a particle and a wave.

Waves of Matter

In showing that the waves which formed electromagnetism could also be seen as particles, quantum theory suddenly blurred the line between these two ideas. If there is no distinction between matter and wave, then what classical ideas are left for physicists? Where could a line be drawn between one thing and another?

Puzzling as it may be, it does seem to be the case that in quantum theory something can be two things at once.

This train of thought led French physicist Louis de Broglie to theorize that not only light but even matter itself may exhibit the properties of both particles and waves. De Broglie figured out mathematically all the factors involved in electron orbits that had been established over the years—their energy, their momentum, the shape of their orbits—and what he found was a new theory of electrons, one which

provided a clear physical meaning to the ambiguity embedded into Pauli's exclusion principle.

De Broglie recognized that the most current atomic theory was still rooted in a distinctly classical perspective, where electrons were "forced" into the preconceived image of little balls of matter spinning around other, larger balls. He reasoned that because even electrons could be viewed as waves, the atom might be far easier to explain in this way.

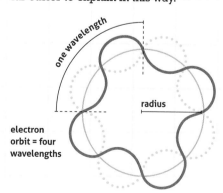

Electron orbits within an atom are determined by specific wavelengths of light—only those orbits permitting whole wavelengths of light are allowed.

If an electron is viewed as a wave, then the distance at which each electron orbits the nucleus of an atom will correspond to the size of its wave, and only orbits in which whole waves would fit could exist. An electron couldn't possibly occupy any other orbit, because as it gained and lost quanta of energy (in the form of photons), its wavelength would either increase or decrease accordingly. The entire notion of specific electron energy levels was readily explained in this new model.

A New Mechanics

·······················

What was needed now was a new system of mechanics, analogous to the laws of Newton or Maxwell, which would govern all particles subject to this quantum behavior and allow physicists to make predictions using these new ideas.

Austrian physicist Erwin Schrödinger began his own work on a wave theory of particles at roughly the same time as De Broglie, but did not publish it until a year later. In 1926, Schrödinger expanded further upon this enticing theory of wave–particle duality. The Schrödinger equation

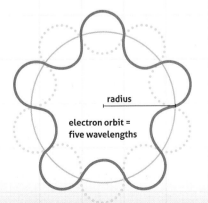

radius

electron orbit =
five wavelengths

WAVES OF WHAT?

Perhaps the most important aspect of the Schrödinger equation was that it sought to remove entirely the concept of quantum mechanical objects (such as photons, electrons, or any other particle) being real, physical objects at all. The waves in quantum mechanics are not physical waves, but waves of pure probability. These waves allow us to measure the chances, at any given time, of finding a particle at a certain place. Though inadvertently, Schrödinger's work led to some of the most difficult questions about what matter actually consists of.

asserted that all matter—not just electrons—could be seen as having an associated wave function. This far-reaching piece of mathematics provided a consistent method by which the state of any quantum system at any given time could be fully calculated.

Schrödinger's equation can be seen as one of the most important moments in twentieth-century physics, providing the solid mathematical basis upon which the debate over quantum physics in the 1920s and '30s would rest. It allowed physicists studying the atomic world to explain and to predict with some accuracy the quantum behavior of subatomic particles.

Werner Heisenberg

Werner Heisenberg infused the world of physics with uncertainty. Though perhaps unintentionally, his work helped to define the very limits of what human beings can and cannot know. A brilliant quantum physicist, Heisenberg helped to found the Copenhagen interpretation of quantum mechanics, which continues to aid physicists even today in defining the methods and meanings of quantum physics.

A Child Prodigy

Werner Heisenberg was born in 1901 in Würzburg, Germany, the son of Dr. August Heisenberg (a professor of Greek at the University of Munich) and Annie Wecklein.

Heisenberg was a child prodigy, mastering the piano at a young age and driven to the pursuit of science by his father's encouragement. As a teenager he taught himself calculus and became engrossed by the challenges presented by physics.

At the University of Munich he studied theoretical physics under the famous Arnold Sommerfeld and alongside Wolfgang Pauli. He also traveled to Göttingen to study under Max Born, who would provide considerable aid to Heisenberg in developing his theories.

Heisenberg received his PhD from Munich in 1923 and returned to Göttingen to assist Max Born. In the mid-1920s he also worked with Niels Bohr at Copenhagen.

Matrix Mechanics and Uncertainty

In 1925 Heisenberg began to develop an entirely new and complete system of quantum mechanics known as "matrix mechanics." This system used the relatively unknown mathematics

of matrices in order to solve quantum-mechanical problems.

Heisenberg published his paper, alongside Max Born and Pascual Jordan, in 1926. The following year, these new methods of calculation led Heisenberg to perhaps his most memorable achievement—the Heisenberg uncertainty principle (see pp. 112–113), which defined the limits of human knowledge in regard to quantum particles. That same year Heisenberg was appointed head of the physics department at the University of Leipzig, where he would remain well into World War II. He traveled widely in the 1930s, and in 1932 he was awarded the Nobel Prize in Physics for "the creation of quantum mechanics."

The War and After

In 1941, with World War II in full swing, Heisenberg was appointed Professor of Physics at the University of Berlin and Director of the Kaiser Wilhelm Institute for Physics there.

While many physicists (especially those of Jewish heritage, such as Einstein and Born) had either fled Germany or been forcibly removed from their positions by the Nazis, Heisenberg remained loyal to his nation and to the Nazi party, forever marring his standing among the world's scientists.

There is much debate as to what kind of work Heisenberg performed during the war, especially in regard to the Nazis' atomic bomb program. Heisenberg claimed to have actively stalled the bomb program.

After the Allied victory, Heisenberg was arrested and brought to England along with other German scientists. He returned to Germany in 1946 and was appointed director of the Max Planck Institute for Physics and Astrophysics at Göttingen.

In later life Heisenberg worked in the field of thermonuclear physics and on the all-important quest to find a unified theory of elementary particles—a quest which continues to this day. He died of cancer in 1976, at the age of 74, having largely repaired his reputation from the war.

Physicists at a conference in Copenhagen, 1937. The leftmost figures in the front row are Bohr, Heisenberg, and Pauli.

"What we observe is not nature itself, but nature exposed to our method of questioning."

Werner Heisenberg

Heisenberg's Uncertainty Principle

Epistemology is the study of knowledge. It is the broad, open-ended search for answers to such questions as "What is the nature of knowledge?" and "How much are humans capable of knowing?" Humans have long believed that it was in their power to know everything. The Heisenberg uncertainty principle forces us to ask a question which seems more philosophical than scientific: "What can we know?" And the answer is disturbingly simple: "Not nearly as much as we thought."

The Formulation of the Principle

Werner Heisenberg was the first to inform the world that determinacy—a predictable universe operating under wholly consistent laws—does not exist. Within quantum mechanics there are things that we simply cannot know, for nothing is determined. The key to Heisenberg's ultimate achievement was the mathematical method he helped to create. Using this tool, a consistent method for solving quantum problems could be found, without relying on the obsolete equations of classical mechanics.

Complementarity

The uncertainty principle is founded on a concept developed by Niels Bohr known as complementarity. This asserts that certain measurable properties of particles come in pairs.

These properties are so thoroughly intertwined that the measurement of one property has a direct result on the measurement of the other.

The most frequently cited example of this principle in action is the problem of measuring the position and momentum of any given particle at the same time—two complementary properties which, according to the uncertainty principle, can never be known simultaneously. We can know one property or the other, but we can never achieve exact measurements for both. We can discover where an electron is (its position), but we will lose all knowledge of its speed (momentum), and vice versa.

This principle is a logical result of wave–particle duality. An electron can exist as either a wave or a particle, but never both. Some experiments are designed to study an electron as if it was a particle, while others study it as if it was a wave, but no experiment may treat an electron as both a particle and a wave at the same time. When we attempt to find the position of an electron, we are thinking in terms of particles (since a wave isn't readily associated with a single position), while momentum is a measurement of an electron in motion (as a wave). It cannot exist in both forms at the same time.

A Break from the Past

The uncertainty principle was not immediately accepted within the scientific community; Einstein, for one, never fully accepted it.

But Heisenberg had offered a quite revolutionary version of quantum mechanics which made a complete break from the past. It enabled him to solve problems that were made more complex by this greater understanding of the relationship between waves and matter.

Heisenberg's work led to increased understanding of the behavior of quantum particles as well as the complete, utter absence of certainty.

Heisenberg's theory of quantum mechanics was complicated by the fact that it did not operate according to the older mechanical explanations of either particles or waves. Most importantly, it refused to allow precise calculations for such things as the positions of electrons as they orbited atoms. Instead it provided approximations whereby an electron's position was given as an area corresponding to the shape of these waves.

THE PHILOSOPHY OF UNCERTAINTY

The uncertainty principle has over the decades led to an abundance of philosophical questions regarding what exactly quantum mechanics actually means. Questions raised, even by physicists such as Niels Bohr, are certainly intriguing: if something can be both a particle and a wave, then is it really anything at all? If the existence of a particle depends upon our measurement, then does the particle really exist in the first place, or do we cause it to exist by measuring it? What kind of consciousness is required to bring matter into existence? And of course there are many more questions beyond these, all directly resulting from the uncertainty principle.

Paul Dirac

There are few physicists who have shaped the way we look at the subatomic world as dramatically as **Paul Dirac**. Though many of the stories involving Dirac focus on the peculiarities of his personality (which were certainly numerous), his contributions to the study of physics led at long last to a final understanding of electrons (and all other particles) as quantum entities and to the prediction and eventual discovery of antimatter.

The Education of Paul Dirac

Paul Dirac was born in Bristol, England, in 1902. His father was Swiss, his mother English. Even in primary school he showed a remarkable ability in mathematics. He studied electrical engineering at the University of Bristol, and this background would later provide him with a unique perspective on the world and affect the methods by which he performed his physical research. Dirac obtained his engineering degree in 1921, but failed to find a permanent position in this field. Seeking to pursue his love of mathematics, he entered Cambridge University in 1923.

Here he became interested in the new theories of relativity and began to work as a research associate, immediately proving himself to be exceptionally capable at both research and theory. Dirac's first notable foray into quantum mechanics came with an early analysis of Heisenberg's uncertainty principle in 1925, which he recognized as an example of noncommutative algebra (a lesser-known field of mathematics he had studied extensively). He essentially rewrote

A young Paul Dirac at work at his blackboard, attempting to create "beautiful" equations (see p. 117).

Heisenberg's principle using the language of mathematics. This work led to his PhD in 1926, after which he traveled to Copenhagen to work with Niels Bohr and then on to Göttingen to work with Robert Oppenheimer and Max Born, among others.

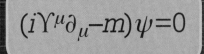

$$(i\Upsilon^{\mu}\partial_{\mu}-m)\psi=0$$

Dirac's equation is commemorated on a plaque in Westminster Abbey, London.

The Anti-Universe

In 1928 Dirac performed his most important work, combining the principle of relativity with quantum mechanics and creating the Dirac equation. This became a tool of incalculable worth for physicists in predicting quantum phenomena. Using this equation, Dirac predicted the existence of a new form of matter—a particle which was identical to the electron, but with an opposite charge. This would become known as the positron. Though contemporaries tended to scoff at the bizarre assertion that an "antiparticle" existed, Dirac went on to propose that not just the electron but all particles possessed "anti" counterparts.

Within just four years the first positron was discovered; Dirac's work on antimatter was vindicated, and won him the 1933 Nobel Prize. Carl Anderson, discoverer of the positron, won the prize for his own discovery in 1936.

Lucasian Professor

In 1930 Dirac was elected a Fellow of the Royal Society. Two years later, he was appointed Lucasian Professor of Mathematics at Cambridge.

While at Cambridge, Dirac changed direction slightly and published papers on cosmological topics. For a time, during World War II, he worked in atomic physics, using the engineering skills he had gained at Bristol University to develop methods of separating uranium for use in both atomic weapons and atomic energy. His later career was spent in the United States. He died at Tallahassee, Florida, in 1984.

▶ KEY WORKS

The Principles of Quantum Mechanics (1930) describes Dirac's own views on quantum mechanics. It supplanted all current textbooks and is still widely used today.

Dirac Prizes in physics, chemistry, and mathematics have been awarded since 1979.

5997 Dirac is an asteroid discovered in 1983 and named in honor of Paul Dirac.

Antimatter

In 1928, Paul Dirac developed his most important contribution to physics: the Dirac equation. Not only did this equation play a crucial role in enabling quantum physicists to calculate the behaviors of particles such as electrons, but it led to the prediction of antimatter. Dirac informed the world that for every particle there also exists an "antiparticle." This idea changed the way physicists viewed all matter.

A Sea of Negative Energy

Dirac began his journey toward antimatter with a version of Einstein's famous equation of mass–energy equivalence ($E = mc^2$). In the case where momentum must be included in the equation (the equation to determine the relativistic energy–momentum relationship), he began with a relatively simple formula:

$$E^2 = m^2c^4 + p^2c^2$$

Dirac knew that this equation had two equally viable answers, with the value of E being either a positive or a negative number. In mathematics, both answers should be given equal weight. This had been understood prior to Dirac, but these negative answers were simply disregarded (for what could possibly be meant by negative amounts of energy?). But Dirac decided to trust the mathematics over the experimental data, wondering what the negative answers might mean.

What Dirac found was rather strange. According to the equation, within an atom there must be both positive energy levels (occupied by normal electrons) and negative energy levels. This led him to declare that all of that "empty" space within and between atoms was not really empty at all. It was a sea of negative-energy electrons.

Dirac went even further, proposing that if this negative material was supplied with enough energy (the

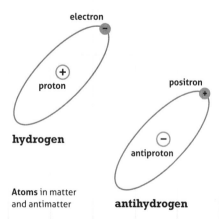

hydrogen

antihydrogen

Atoms in matter and antimatter

required energy can be calculated by Einstein's original equation), a positive-energy particle (such as an electron) could be produced from the negative energy. This process would not only create an electron, but would leave an electron-sized hole in the field of negative energy. Dirac proposed that this hole would appear to any outside observer as a normal electron, positively charged.

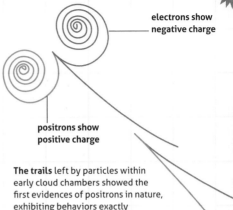

electrons show negative charge

positrons show positive charge

The trails left by particles within early cloud chambers showed the first evidences of positrons in nature, exhibiting behaviors exactly opposite to those of the electron.

Enter the Positron

....

This hypothetical particle became known as the positron. Dirac had no physical justification for this theory at first—he based it on the mathematics, which he trusted. He has been quoted as saying that, "it is more important to have beauty in one's equations than to have them fit experiment."

Dirac and his equations were finally justified four years after his original proposal, when the first traces of real-life positrons were found by Carl Anderson in 1932.

The positron, however, is certainly not the only antiparticle. Dirac's theory holds true for other pieces of antimatter, however large— antiprotons and antineutrons, for example. Every particle possesses an antiparticle counterpart, and many of these have been found in experiments.

It now appears that antimatter is not as exotic as it once seemed. We have reason to believe that a number of different antiparticles are produced

by cosmic rays (though these particles are extremely short-lived), and that antineutrinos and positrons are consistently produced by the nuclear reactions within the Sun.

ANNIHILATION

The existence of antimatter poses an interesting and important question: if it is being produced in nature, why do we not see more of it? The simple answer is that because matter and antimatter are oppositely charged, when antimatter is produced it is very quickly drawn toward matter. The two particles collide and are immediately annihilated, turning into pure energy. This is where the potential for producing energy using antimatter comes in.

The complicated answer goes all the way back to the Big Bang, asking why there is more matter than antimatter in the first place—and we have not yet answered this question entirely.

Probability and Quantum Mechanics

Quantum physics makes it quite clear that a particle cannot exist as both a wave and a particle at the same time, and that a particle may possess both wave-like and particle-like properties. But what does this mean? What is really happening to an electron when it "spreads out" into a wave as it orbits within an atom? Where does the particle go? And what implications does this have on the material world that we call home?

Waves of Chance

Bearing in mind Schrödinger's wave equation (see p. 109) and the principle of uncertainty (pp. 112–113), we must accept that the wave described by Schrödinger is not a physical wave that describes the motion of an electron, but a wave function that describes the probability of finding an electron at a given location at a given time. When we say that a particle moves as a wave, we mean a wave of oscillating probability. If we were to pick a point within that wave at a given moment, we could use Schrödinger's equation to calculate the probability of finding a particle at that location (even if the particle doesn't necessarily exist until we actually look for it). The act of finding a particle in the midst of a probability wave is often referred to as "collapsing the wave function," for finding the particle forces all probability to disappear.

Making Use of Probability

So how can we find a way to use this seemingly frustrating aspect of quantum mechanics? The answer is to stop looking at the behavior of individual particles and begin looking at the problem as a whole, in terms of statistics and probability.

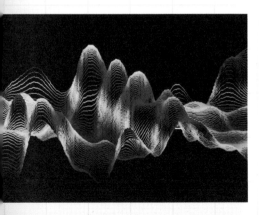

Images from scanning tunneling microscopes are visual representations of atomic structure.

A familiar analogy is flipping a coin. On any given flip you have a 50% chance of being right or wrong—an equal chance of either heads or tails. Your chances of guessing each flip individually are not very good. But what if you flip the coin 100 times, guessing that about 50% will result in heads and 50% in tails? Statistically speaking, your results should be much more accurate. Now, what if you decided to flip the coin a million times? It is a hard and fast rule of statistics that the larger the sample, the higher the accuracy. This same rule holds true for particles.

The existence of uncertainty on a microscopic level, therefore, does not necessarily prevent us from making measurements or enhancing our understanding of how particles behave. It's just that when doing so, we are forced to do it in a statistical sense, asking not about the behavior of individual particles, but about a system as a whole.

By accepting the truth of wave–particle duality and the uncertainty principle, some of the greatest advances in physical theory have been made, from the principles of quantum electrodynamics in the 1940s and '50s to the ongoing efforts to find the ultimate theories that govern everything. We move forward in physics only by accepting our own limitations and learning to use them to our advantage.

QUANTUM TUNNELING

One of the most unusual side effects of viewing quantum waves as merely waves of probability is that it allows particles to engage in some rather peculiar behavior. For example, if a probability wave extends beyond an "impassable" barrier, there is a chance that the particle may suddenly "jump" to the other side. This phenomenon is called "quantum tunneling," and lest it be written off as mere conjecture, this fact of nature has been extremely well documented and even put to use in modern circuitry and in such tools as the scanning tunneling microscope.

classical physics

electron particle hits barrier . . .

. . . electron is reflected 100% of the time.

quantum physics

electron wave hits barrier . . .

. . . particle is most likely reflected, but there's a small probability that it will "tunnel" through and spontaneously reappear on the other side.

Practical Quantum Mechanics

Sure, quantum mechanics is interesting, with all its outlandish claims that seem to describe a world other than our own, yet which appears to be true. But is it merely fascinating, or is there a practical side to it as well? Is there any point in studying quantum mechanics other than to satisfy our curiosity about the physical world? Actually, it is quite possible for quantum mechanics to have a direct effect on the world as we know it.

A Tool for Understanding

Since everything is made up of atoms, held together and acted upon by forces, understanding the principles which govern these things allows us a better understanding of the world around us. But more than this, understanding how quantum mechanics comes into play in everyday life can actually help us to make things better!

Every object incorporating modern circuitry (which today seems to be nearly every object you can find) is essentially quantum-mechanical, making use of semiconductors, transistors, diodes, and other miniature devices which take advantage of principles such as quantum chemistry and quantum tunneling. The truth is that quantum mechanics is everywhere, and we are only just learning how these principles can lead to better products and better manufacturing.

A Tool to Study Quantum Physics

Quantum mechanics helps us to understand quantum physics. Many of the tools we use to study it are only made possible by quantum physics.

For example, the scanning tunneling microscope uses the wavelength of electrons to visualize a smaller world than would be possible with even the most powerful optical microscope. In this technology, a metal tip is positioned with incredible precision only a tiny distance (a matter of only a few angstroms, or ten-billionths of a meter) from the substance (often a metal) being studied. When a charge is applied to the tip, electrons are drawn from the source and are able to tunnel across this vacuum to the tip. The patterns of this tunneling can then be analyzed by a computer, which translates the data into a visual representation of the atomic structure of the subject.

Apart from giving us some of our first images of actual atoms, these microscopes have enabled us to manipulate individual atoms in order to place them in certain patterns, forming the beginnings of nanotechnology—an entirely new branch of science which promises to deliver new materials of unbelievable strength, not to mention significant advances in medicine.

Quantum Computers

Advances in quantum mechanics have led to continued improvements in computing power, but they may one day lead to quantum computers.

Where today's computers work with bits (binary units) of information, quantum computers would use qubits (quantum binary units), which hold the potential to work faster and store far more information. Where a bit can only exist as either a 1 or a 0, a qubit can exist in a "superposition" of both states at once.

It has been predicted that even a relatively simple quantum computer has the potential to perform operations millions of times faster than today's most modern computers. All that stands in our way now is one of the most difficult engineering challenges ever faced by mankind: to manipulate individual quantum particles in such a precise way that they retain their quantum-mechanical features while at the same time allowing the storage and processing of vast amounts of information. Easier said than done!

SCHRÖDINGER'S CAT

Erwin Schrödinger devised a famous thought experiment to express the paradoxical nature of quantum theory. Don't try this at home!

Imagine a cat placed in a sealed box, along with some radioactive element that has a 50% chance of decaying (emitting one particle) over the course of an hour. Also in the box are a Geiger counter (a device to detect radioactive decay) and a vial of poison gas. A device is rigged up that will break open the vial of poison if the Geiger counter detects a radioactive particle.

When the box is opened after an hour, there is a 50 : 50 chance that the cat will be alive or dead. But what happens in the box when no one is looking? According to some interpretations of quantum theory, the cat should be both dead and alive—the two states exist at once until the box is opened! In quantum mechanics, reason and logic are not to be trusted.

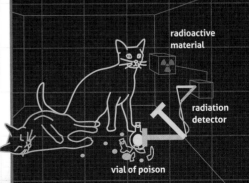

radioactive material

radiation detector

vial of poison

7

Modern Physics

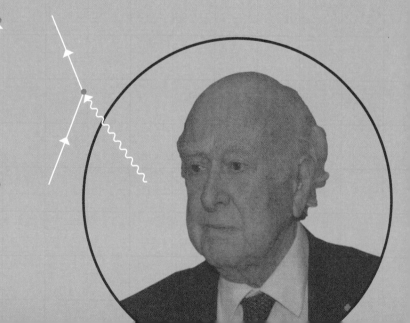

This final chapter surveys the state of physics today. What are the most exciting fields of study? How is research in physics currently being performed? And perhaps most importantly, where is physics going to take us in the future? Within this chapter are explanations of the current state of particle physics, an introduction to the expensive but all-important particle accelerators, a look into the mysteries of black holes, and a glimpse into the most promising theories of everything.

Richard Feynman

Richard Feynman was one of the most brilliant and unique characters in twentieth-century physics. Though a Nobel Prize-winner and one of the finest minds of his generation, Feynman was also known for his wit, curiosity, and sense of adventure. Whether moving to Brazil and mastering the bongo drum, traveling to Mexico and learning to translate Mayan mathematics, or learning to break into the safes at the Los Alamos nuclear facility during World War II, Feynman's adventures are legendary.

Rise to Prominence

Richard Feynman was born in Queens, New York, in 1918. When he was ten the family moved to Far Rockaway, New York. By his own account, Feynman was greatly inspired by his father and developed a curiosity about the natural world—a curiosity that took deep root. He began studying at the Massachusetts Institute of Technology in 1935, obtaining his BSc in mathematics in 1939. Only then did he move into physics.

Feynman pursued his graduate work at Princeton University, where he first became interested in Paul Dirac's work on quantum mechanics and began to apply some of his own original thoughts to these theories. His doctoral work at Princeton led Feynman, at just 23 years old, to think about the question of electron and electromagnetic interactions in a new and creative way. This work culminated in an original and exciting explanation of quantum mechanics known as quantum electrodynamics (see pp. 126–127).

Another important invention was the Feynman diagram. This was a simple way for physicists to graphically represent complex mathematical equations and simplify complicated phenomena. Feynman won the Nobel Prize in 1965 for his work in quantum electrodynamics, sharing the award with Julian Schwinger and Japanese physicist Sin-Itiro Tomonaga.

World War II and the Manhattan Project

Feynman was invited to join the race to build the atomic bomb, and moved to Los Alamos to join some of the greatest minds in physics.

Though grief-stricken by the death of his first wife from tuberculosis, Feynman returned to his work, witnessing the first ever test of a nuclear explosion in the New Mexican desert. He also took some time here and there to test the security at the research facility—by learning to pick the locks of the safes which held the nation's most important nuclear secrets.

Later Life and Work

After the war, Feynman was appointed as a professor of theoretical physics, first at Cornell University and then, in 1950, at the California Institute of Technology, which would be his home for the remainder of his life. Before taking up his post at Caltech, Feynman spent ten months on sabbatical in Brazil, where he avidly took up playing the bongo drum.

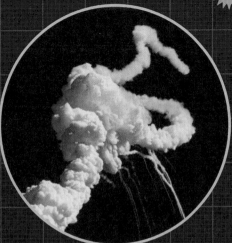

The *Challenger* space shuttle disaster, and the subsequent investigation, placed Richard Feynman firmly in the public eye.

Alongside his work in quantum electrodynamics at Caltech, Feynman branched into other subjects, such as a theory of partons which led fellow Caltech professor Murray Gell-Mann to propose that some particles were made up of even smaller quarks (see p.131). He joined the committee to investigate the *Challenger* space shuttle disaster in 1986, demonstrating live on television the failure of the shuttle's O-rings. Feynman died in 1988, at the age of 69, from stomach cancer.

BOOKS

Richard Feynman was perhaps the most approachable of the prominent scientists of the twentieth century. He published numerous books in his lifetime, several of which are easily accessed by the common reader. Two of these books are filled with humorous stories and scientific anecdotes:

Surely You're Joking, Mr. Feynman!: Adventures of a Curious Character (1985) covers topics from safe-cracking to the Brazilian education system, by way of the Manhattan Project and meetings with great men.

What Do You Care What Other People Think? Further Adventures of a Curious Character (1988) is largely concerned with his investigation of the *Challenger* space shuttle disaster, but it also has its lighter moments.

Quantum Electrodynamics

Richard Feynman described his greatest achievement, quantum electrodynamics (QED), in his book *The Strange Theory of Light and Matter*. Strange it most certainly is, but its strangeness is surely overshadowed by its accuracy. It is difficult to overemphasize just how all-encompassing QED is—practically any observable event in our universe must in some way be governed by the laws regarding light and electrons.

What Is QED?

Which unfathomably complicated concepts and sets of laws must one come to terms with in order to even begin to understand such a far-reaching theory as QED? What new feats of learning must we achieve? In fact, QED involves just three simple actions:

Action #1: An electron goes from place to place.

Action #2: A photon goes from place to place.

Action #3: An electron absorbs or emits a photon.

That's truly all there is to it—just those three steps, none of which introduces any particularly new ideas which have not been discussed elsewhere in this book. Every action and reaction we observe in the universe can, in one way or another, be simplified to just those three primary actions, which form the backbone of QED.

It is only when we attempt to put QED to use that we realize its true value, both in explaining the material world and in revealing some of its deepest mysteries.

The three possible events in QED: an electron moves; a photon moves; and an electron absorbs or emits a photon.

time

electron   photon   photon emission or absorption

space

The Sum Over Histories

As stated before (but it deserves to be said again), quantum electro-dynamics helps us to explain everything. Want to know just why light reflects off a mirror or why items placed in water appear distorted; or why we see mirages on the road on a hot day; or how lenses work to focus light; or how atoms bind together electromagnetically? The answers lie in QED and those three simple actions listed earlier.

Both the value and the mystery of QED come from looking at some very peculiar questions regarding these actions. For instance, as an electron moves from one position to another, we must ask if there are any specific laws which might prohibit it from taking anything but the most direct path. In fact, there are no such laws. An electron (or a photon) may take any path it chooses from one place to another, no matter how erratic or improbable it might seem.

In fact, the only way to solve problems involving the path of an electron is to take into consideration every path that it could possibly take. Every possibility must be taken into account, and their individual probabilities must be added together in order to mathematically explain what is actually observed. Electrons (and photons) do not always move in perfectly straight lines, but wander about in strange, curving paths, emitting and absorbing photons and changing both their speed and direction.

Only when all of these possible paths are added together (and they are literally infinite in number) do we find that the path of least time is (usually) the path that is observed. Feynman called this method of treating all possibilities as reality the "sum over histories" approach.

FEYNMAN DIAGRAMS

One of Feynman's most memorable contributions to science, and particularly to QED, is the Feynman diagram. This diagram simplifies things by converting the normal four dimensions of space-time into a much simpler two-dimensional graph, in which the two dimensions are space and time. These diagrams help theorists to visualize particular actions and interactions, and then to calculate the probabilities of these events using some very intuitive mathematical tricks developed by Feynman (and refined by others). Though the mathematics of QED is undeniably difficult, these handy little diagrams do much to help the medicine go down a bit more easily.

Feynman simplified every physical event into just two dimensions—space and time. Space is the horizontal axis and time is vertical.

Particle Acceleration

In late 2009 the largest particle accelerator ever built (indeed, the largest scientific instrument ever made), the Large Hadron Collider, went into operation, 574 feet (175 m) underground on the Swiss–French border. This achievement capped off nearly a century of innovative devices which have brought us to understand the world of particles on a far deeper level than we could ever have imagined.

What Particle Accelerators Do

Einstein's famous equation, $E = mc^2$ (see pp. 92–93), states that pure energy can theoretically be transformed into matter. Experimentation showed physicists that with enough energy, any particle could be created—the more energy, the more massive the particle. This is the theory that lies behind all of particle physics.

Any physicist attempting to find a particle simply needs to produce the amount of energy necessary for that particle to be created. This is what particle accelerators do. They speed up particles and slam them together, producing energy out of which second-generation particles are created. These can be detected and analyzed using a number of devices, such as the cloud chamber (a pressurized chamber in which a particle's ionization trails can be photographed), the bubble chamber (in which particles leave trails of bubbles in a liquid), or the more modern spark chambers or proportional wire detectors which use computer-assisted detection.

The First Accelerator

In 1912, Austrian-American physicist Victor Hess was the first to carry detectors with him in a hot-air balloon and to discover cosmic rays. These rays of particles shower Earth from all corners of outer space at unbelievably high speeds, originating from sources such as solar flares, distant supernovas, or nearby stars.

Cosmic rays travel at speeds very close to the speed of light, smashing into the particles in our atmosphere and resulting in the formation of secondary particles which can be detected here on Earth. The limitation is that there is no way of controlling just when and where these rays will strike.

Man-Made Accelerators

The first artificial particle accelerator, the cyclotron, was invented in 1929 by Ernest Lawrence at the University of California, Berkeley. Particle accelerators such as this fire a beam of particles at high speed, which collide with other particles inside a detector.

Today, particle accelerators come in two standard varieties: linear and circular. Linear accelerators require a perfectly straight beam of particles, which is accelerated using finely tuned electromagnets. The particles are sent at high speeds into other particles near a detector, where the results are recorded and analyzed. The longest linear accelerator in the world today is the 2-mile-long Stanford Linear Accelerator Center in Menlo Park, California.

The largest circular accelerator is the Large Hadron Collider (LHC) near Geneva, Switzerland, completed in 2008. This ambitious project is intended to discover

MEDICAL ACCELERATORS

Cyclotrons are still used today in some hospitals. Finely tuned particle beams from these machines have frequently been used to target and destroy cancerous tissue in patients. Accelerators are also used in positron emission tomography (PET). This uses positrons produced in small accelerators to detect gamma rays inside the human body in order to reconstruct three-dimensional images of the body's internal structures. In many ways, physics is invaluable in modern medicine.

A PET image of a live human brain. Images like this are important in diagnosing cancer and brain disease.

several new particles which have been theorized, such as the elusive Higgs boson (see p. 133). In a circular accelerator, particles may potentially travel through the same system forever, accelerating closer and closer to the speed of light until there is no longer enough power to accelerate them further. Within these colossal machines are potential answers to many of the universe's mysteries, such as why particles have mass, how all the particles and forces are related to one another, and just what the early universe looked like.

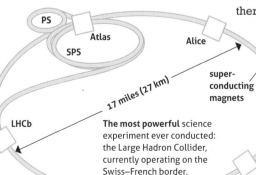

PS

Atlas

SPS

Alice

super-conducting magnets

17 miles (27 km)

LHCb

The most powerful science experiment ever conducted: the Large Hadron Collider, currently operating on the Swiss–French border.

CMS

The Particle Zoo

In the biological sciences, there is an important field of research known as taxonomy (derived from the Greek *taxis*, and meaning "the law of order"). Taxonomists attempt to classify plants and animals according to their various features, into such categories as kingdom, phylum, genus, and species. Only in the past half-century has a very similar field of study arisen in physics, which we might simply call atomic taxonomy—a push toward classification of the many subatomic particles.

The Glory Days of Particle Physics

The middle decades of the twentieth century were some of the most fruitful ever known in physics. They saw the creation of progressively more effective methods of particle acceleration and detection, along with the discovery of ever more complicated and unexpected physical laws.

Year by year, dozens of new particles were being discovered, classified, studied, and pondered over. Sometimes a new theory would lead to the search for a new particle (as was the case with the positron in 1932 and the pion in 1947), while at other points a chance discovery of a new particle would lead physicists to search for a theoretical explanation.

Though particles may be classified in numerous ways—for example, by mass and charge—today it is most common to classify them all into three distinct groups: leptons, mesons, and baryons.

Leptons

Leptons were originally considered to be the lightest of the atomic particles (the name comes from the Greek word *leptos*, meaning "light"), though later it was found that some leptons are really not very light at all. Today we believe that six leptons exist: the electron, the muon, the tau, the electron neutrino, the muon neutrino, and the tau neutrino. Of these six, only the electron and the electron neutrino are common in the universe. The others (such as the muon and the tau, which are essentially just really heavy electrons) have been found using particle accelerators, or in high-speed cosmic ray collisions in Earth's atmosphere.

The neutrinos are extremely light, neutrally charged particles which arise out of certain nuclear processes, such as radioactive decay. They are notably difficult to study experimentally, though researchers have managed to find clever means of tracking them down.

Mesons

Next step up from leptons are the mesons (from the Greek word *mesos*, meaning "middle"). Mesons often serve to carry force between other particles. Among the mesons are the pion (which carries force between protons and neutrons, allowing the atomic nucleus to stick together), the kaon, the j/psi, and many more. Physicists have discovered well over 20 other mesons, though most of them possess lifetimes far too short to serve any real purpose.

Baryons

The final particles are known as baryons (with a name meaning "heavy" in Greek). This family consists of the familiar nucleons—the proton and the neutron—along with more than a hundred lesser-known and seemingly inconsequential particles (plus antiparticles) such as the Delta, Xi, Lambda, Sigma, and Omega, each of which comes in a wide array of varieties (the Xi particle alone comes in at least twenty varieties).

Though the sheer number of baryons might seem imposing on the surface, we may take comfort in the fact that only a couple of them—the proton and the neutron—really serve

any purpose in our everyday lives. The others exist, it seems, only to add beauty to our theories.

Quarks

In the late 1960s, American physicist Murray Gell-Mann simplified matters considerably by discovering that two of these "families" of particles—the mesons and the baryons—are actually composed of even smaller particles, called quarks, which are only six in number (just as there are six total leptons). They are: up quark, down quark, strange quark, charm quark, top quark, and bottom quark.

All mesons are made up of two quarks—one regular quark and one antiquark (for antimatter versions of quarks are known to exist, just like every other known particle). All of the baryons are made up of three regular quarks. For example, a proton is made up of two up quarks and one down quark, while a neutron is made of two down quarks and one up quark.

In addition to the six leptons and six quarks, there are a few force-carrying particles (such as the photon), all of which constitute the entire particle zoo!

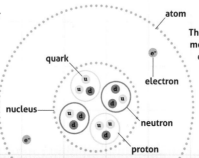

The current atomic model, in which electrons orbit the nucleus. The nucleus is made up of protons and neutrons, which are themselves made of quarks.

The Standard Model

The standard model of particle physics is, for the time being, the culmination of all that we know about the smallest things in the universe. Under this model we have succeeded in simplifying absolutely everything in the physical universe down to just two dozen particles and four total forces. Though there are a few holes in this theory, the standard model remains today as the most successful, complete model of physics ever developed. But the future, as always, is uncertain.

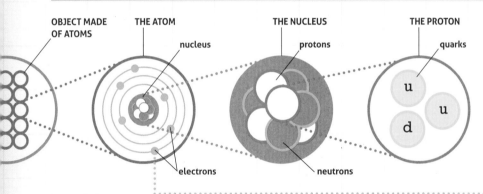

OBJECT MADE OF ATOMS | THE ATOM — nucleus, electrons | THE NUCLEUS — protons, neutrons | THE PROTON — quarks

Particles and Forces

In the standard model as it is presently formulated, there are 17 total particles (29 including antiparticles). These particles can be divided into three groups: leptons, quarks, and gauge bosons.

The particles are acted upon by the four forces described opposite: the strong and weak nuclear forces, the electromagnetic force, and the force of gravity. Every action and reaction in the universe can be reduced to these four forces.

Leptons

The six known leptons include the common electron and its larger cousins, the muon and the tau. Each of these has a neutrino counterpart: the electron neutrino, muon neutrino, and tau neutrino. In the standard model, each of these pairs belongs to a particular "generation." First-generation (the least massive) are the electron and electron neutrino; the muon and muon neutrino are second generation; and tau and tau neutrino are third (most massive).

- Electron
- Muon
- Tau
- Electron neutrino
- Muon neutrino
- Tau neutrino

Quarks

The six quarks are divided into generations according to their differing masses. The first generation of quarks includes the two most common, the up quark and the down quark. The second generation comprises the strange quark and charm quark, and the final generation consists of the top quark and the bottom quark. The branch of physics that deals with quarks is known as quantum chromodynamics.

- Up
- Down
- Charm
- Strange
- Top
- Boson

The Forces

The Strong Nuclear Force

This, the strongest of all the fundamental forces, is responsible for holding together the atomic nucleus. It is the force by which quarks are held together within protons and neutrons, and by which the protons and neutrons themselves are bound to one another. Though the strength of the nuclear force is far beyond anything that we experience every day, it is only effective over a very short range—about the size of the atomic nucleus, in fact.

The Electromagnetic Force

Readily present and visible everywhere you look, this force provides us with power, of course; but it is also the very reason that matter exists in the first place. It is this force that binds atoms together to form all compounds and substances. We all consist of little more than atoms held together electro-magnetically. We ought to be grateful, therefore, that electromagnetism is as strong as it is.

The Weak Nuclear Force

Its purpose is not to hold things together, but to break them apart. It is this force that causes atoms to be unstable, to decay, and to split apart. It is because of the weak nuclear force that nuclear weapons and energy are possible and, more importantly, that the Sun shines. Like the strong force, the weak force is only effective at very short distances within the atomic nucleus. It is just a bit weaker than electromagnetism.

Gravity

By far the weakest of all the forces (at 10^{39} times weaker than the strong nuclear force), gravity is surely the force that we are most familiar with. Yet it is also perhaps the least understood. Gravity has proven monumentally difficult to factor into the standard model, and is the main reason this model is considered a work in progress.

Gauge bosons

These are the force-carrying particles of the subatomic world. Each force is associated with its own gauge bosons, which can be exchanged between other particles in order to keep them stuck together (or to pull them apart). The photon carries the electromagnetic force, gluons carry the strong nuclear force, and the W and Z bosons convey the weak nuclear force. The discovery of the Higgs boson, which is thought to give mass to all of the other particles, was announced in 2013 and is expected to be confirmed soon. More gauge bosons probably remain to be discovered, including the graviton, which conveys the gravitational force.

- Photon
- W boson
- Gluon
- Z boson

Black Holes

Black holes are not particularly new to science—the possibility that black holes could exist was first considered in the eighteenth century. But it was not until the latter half of the twentieth century that our understanding advanced significantly, when cosmologists began to look at the universe in detail through the lens of Einstein's general theory of relativity.

What Is a Black Hole?

A black hole is not, in fact, a hole; rather, it is the opposite. Whereas a hole may be defined as the absence of substance, a black hole is a body of mass so very dense, with such a great gravitational attraction, that nothing, not even light, may travel fast enough to escape its grasp. Black holes are like astronomical whirlpools that suck in everything that comes near.

Though it was the work of Einstein in 1915 that gave an insight into the details of black holes, credit for the first theoretical musing that such things might exist should go to the eighteenth-century clergyman and geologist, John Michell.

Drawing on his understanding of escape velocity (the speed that an object must reach in order to overcome gravity), Michell considered that if an object had sufficient mass—and thus an escape velocity greater than the speed of light—then even light wouldn't be moving fast enough to escape from such an object. The object would be what we now call a black hole.

Michell never really theorized that such an object truly did exist—at the time it was just an interesting idea.

> "Black holes are regions of space where the gravity is so high that the fabric of space and time has curved back on itself, taking the exit doors with it."
>
> — **American astrophysicist Neil deGrasse Tyson**

Black Holes Today

After the development of general relativity, the concept of black holes achieved an entirely new scientific foundation. Based on Einstein's accepted theory of gravity as warped space-time, scientists could now explore how black holes might actually form from the collapse of large stars, and what kind of effect this might have on nearby objects (which was thought to be the only way they could be detected). In the 1920s, German physicist Karl Schwarzschild explored the mathematics behind black holes and developed the Schwarzschild radius, a rather simple equation which showed how the diameter of a black hole changes by way of its mass.

The term "black hole" was only coined by Caltech physicist John Wheeler (to replace the previous term, "frozen star") in 1967, and it quickly caught on as others, such as Stephen Hawking (see pp. 136–137), took up the study of these peculiar objects. Hawking was the first to recognize that black holes aren't entirely black, with his discovery of what has become known as Hawking radiation.

Although black holes have not yet been seen by way of Hawking radiation, their presence in the universe is confirmed by observations of their effects on other astronomical objects (large gravitational attractions with seemingly nothing at the center, or binary systems of which only one body can be seen, for example). It is believed that supermassive black holes may act as the center of gravity for many, if not all, of the galaxies in the universe, including our own.

Creating Black Holes

Today, particle accelerators have become powerful enough that tiny black holes may potentially be produced on Earth. These micro-black holes are similar to those which are said to have existed at the formation of the universe. They last only for an exceedingly short time before disappearing (they evaporate by giving off Hawking radiation), thus giving physicists only an instant to explore their mysteries.

While there is some controversy regarding the wisdom of creating black holes on Earth, there is excitement among physicists as to where such explorations might lead in regard to deciphering some of the fundamental mysteries of the universe.

Within Einstein's general theory of relativity, a black hole is a place where space-time becomes infinitely warped, creating a literal "hole" in space-time out of which nothing can escape.

Stephen Hawking

Most people know only a few things about Stephen Hawking: that he is one of today's most brilliant scientists and that he suffers from a rare and debilitating disease which has left him confined to a wheelchair and unable to speak but for the aid of a sophisticated computer. What is less commonly known is the depth of his contribution to the world of physics, both in terms of his physical and mathematical knowledge and of his desire to further the scientific dialogue. Hawking has been instrumental in inspiring popular interest in science.

Personal Tragedy

Stephen Hawking was born in Oxford, England, in 1942. His father urged him to pursue scientific studies and, after looking into both biology and medicine, Hawking decided to pursue mathematics and physics.

In 1959 Hawking was awarded a scholarship to Oxford University. He achieved a First Class degree in 1962, with a specialization in physics. Hawking then attended Cambridge University, studying general relativity and cosmology.

In 1963 Hawking was diagnosed with amyotrophic lateral sclerosis (ALS, or Lou Gehrig's disease), a condition that attacks the motor neurons, impairing the ability of the brain to communicate with the rest of the body. Doctors predicted that he would not live long enough to complete his studies.

Hawking was married in 1965 to Jane Wilde, an event that he claims gave him the strength to continue fighting for his doctorate. Still his health deteriorated, and by the mid-1970s he had lost the ability to feed himself. Ten years later, almost entirely paralyzed, Hawking suffered from a bout of pneumonia and was given a tracheotomy, which left him unable to communicate except by way of a voice synthesizer. Hawking's early life was dramatized in the movie *The Theory of Everything* (2014).

Scientific Achievements

As his condition began to stabilize, Hawking pursued his studies with distinction, receiving his PhD in 1966 and embarking on research which would contribute more to our

▶ KEY WORKS

A BRIEF HISTORY OF TIME:
One of Hawking's most memorable achievements does not fall into the category of formal science at all, but is a book intended for general audiences: 1988's *A Brief History of Time*. This book, which covers such intimidating topics as general relativity, black holes, the Big Bang,

understanding of gravity and the cosmos than that of any other physicist since Einstein.

Hawking's first major contribution came with his theory of singularities. He used Einstein's theory of general relativity (see pp. 94–97) to theorize that a point may exist in which both space and time become, essentially, infinite. This is the basic idea which governs our current understanding of both black holes and the point in space-time which existed just before the "Big Bang" brought our present universe into existence.

Hawking's theory of black holes led to important new facets of our understanding of these peculiar objects. For example, according to quantum mechanics, black holes give off trace amounts of heat (which became known as Hawking radiation), which contradicted the previously held belief that nothing could ever escape from a black hole. He also predicted that black holes need not be immense, but may be even as small as subatomic particles.

> Stephen Hawking's research would contribute more to our understanding of gravity and the cosmos than that of any other physicist since Einstein.

Hawking was Lucasian Professor of Physics at Cambridge from 1979 to 2009. He remains active in physics more than half a century after his doctors had told him he would not survive to complete his degree.

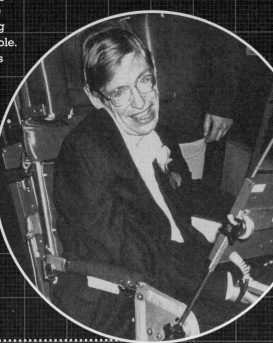

Dr. Stephen Hawking: a brilliant mind that refuses to be stifled by a paralyzed body.

and predictive cosmology, is one of the best-selling books of all time, having sold over 10,000,000 copies since its release. The book is essential reading for anyone desiring a clear, concise explanation of modern cosmology from one of the greatest minds in that (or any other) field.

A New Cosmology

Cosmology is a branch of physics on a macroscopic scale. It is the physics of the universe as a whole; it is the shape, structure, behavior, past, present, and future of everything. It is only in the past few decades that astronomical observations have afforded physicists enough knowledge of the universe to begin solving some of these problems, though the search for answers has often just led us to even more questions.

The Expanding Universe

One thing that seems fairly certain is that the universe is expanding. This does not mean merely that stars and galaxies are moving away from each other in space, but that the very fabric of space itself is in the process of expanding. Galaxies are moving away from each other as a result of the Big Bang.

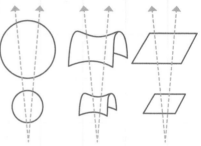

The three possible shapes of our universe: a "finite but boundless" sphere, a curved "saddle" shape, or a nearly curveless shape.

DARK MATTER AND DARK ENERGY

A major stumbling-block to measuring the density of the universe has been the discovery of mysterious and invisible substances which seem to permeate it, affectionately referred to as "dark matter" and "dark energy." Measurements of distant galaxies have revealed the presence of huge amounts of mass hidden somewhere in the universe which we can neither see nor detect. In fact, it is estimated that these dark substances constitute as much as 80 to 90% of all matter in the known universe. It is shocking that something so omnipresent could have escaped our notice for so long, but such seems to be the case. There are theories concerning the nature of dark matter and dark energy, and it is hoped that continued research in particle accelerators might lead to some concrete answers, but for now it remains a mystery right out of science fiction.

The expansion of the universe was discovered in the 1920s when Edwin Hubble noted that the color spectrum of distant galaxies seemed to be shifted slightly toward the red end of the spectrum. This was called a redshift—a telltale sign that galaxies were moving farther apart.

This expanding view of the universe fits in well with the mathematics of general relativity. It gives us a more accurate description of the current state of the universe and provides insight into both past and future.

The Past
•••••••••••

To see the past, we need only to hit the rewind button, which is what physicists have been trying to do for more than half a century now.

If the universe is expanding now, then running time in reverse would see it contracting: stars, planets, and whole galaxies turned back into dense clouds of atoms and molecules, being pulled toward a single location by the all-pervasive force of gravity, their combined masses warping space-time and drawing greater amounts of mass into this location. Finally, after 10 or 20 billion years, everything comes together into a single, tiny area with near-infinite density: a singularity. What may have gone on inside this infinitely dense state of matter is beyond the limits of our present knowledge, but out of it came all of matter, the laws of physics, and the dimensions of space-time themselves.

The Future
•••••••••••••••

To determine what will happen in the universe after we are gone (we're talking many billions of years, most likely), we really only need concrete answers to two questions: how rapidly is the universe expanding now? And what is the average mass density of the universe?

The first question can be calculated to a certain extent using data about the retreat of distant stars and galaxies. The second question has proven harder than we could have imagined (see "Dark Matter and Dark Energy," opposite).

Finding answers to these questions would surely lead us to one of three conclusions:

1 The universe will continue to expand forever until all order in the universe is gone and all matter goes into a state of deep, permanent freeze.

2 The rate of expansion is not that fast and the universe will eventually be able to stop expanding and retain some sort of stability.

3 Eventually the expansion will stop and gravity will lead to contraction, pulling everything back together until the universe collapses in on itself to become a singularity once again (the "Big Crunch" theory).

A Theory of Everything?

It is, undeniably, the ultimate goal of physics to find a single, consistent theory which enables us to understand everything. This is what the dreams of physicists are made on, and it is something that many scientists, from the ancient Greeks to Newton, Einstein, and their successors, have attempted. It has been a long, hard couple of thousand years in the making, but could it be that we now stand on the verge of such a theory?

The Problem of Gravity

The standard model of physics, with its neat list of particles and forces, tells us nearly everything we could want to know about why things are the way they are, but it is not yet complete. It is missing one extremely important addition: gravity.

Sure, gravity appears within the standard model's list of forces, but it doesn't seem to fit. While the other three forces have similarities which suggest that there must be a deep underlying connection between them, we find no such convenient

Perhaps none of these theories is correct. We continue searching, for in physics, as in life, much of the fun lies in the journey rather than the destination.

properties in gravity. Physicists believe that there is a point at which the nuclear forces and electromagnetism must converge and become one. The weak force and electromagnetism have indeed been combined into one force, known as the electroweak force. But it has proven extremely difficult to factor gravity into this model. This seems to be a particularly serious problem.

The Origin of Mass

Another question which has not been answered in full (though there seems to be some hope that it will be soon) is the question of mass. Though mass is fairly simple to measure in many particles, we have not yet been able to determine exactly where this mass comes from. The best guess thus far is that it comes from the interaction of particles with an all-pervasive field in our universe known as the Higgs field (named for physicist Peter Higgs). If this theory is correct, then the Higgs field will naturally, like every other force, have an associated particle, known as the Higgs boson. It is this particle that experimenters hope they have found in the Large Hadron Collider (see pp. 128–129).

apparent mass

particle

Higgs field

Potential Theories of Everything

∙∙∙∙∙∙∙∙∙∙∙∙∙∙∙∙∙∙∙∙

String theory represents one of the best-known of the potential theories of everything, though in actuality it encapsulates a multitude of overlapping ideas. "String theory" refers to any of several dozen potential models, each of which has just one thing in common: they believe that everything can be best understood in terms of tiny, one-dimensional strings and their vibrations.

Left: the British Nobel laureate Peter Higgs (b. 1929).

Below: An image from the LHC showing a computer model of two protons colliding.

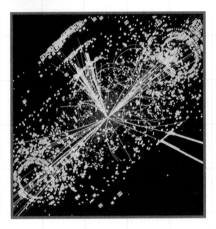

That is string theory at its most simplistic: looping, knotting, dividing, vibrating strings which together form all space-time and matter in the universe, being the cause of all the great variation and order that we see in the universe around us. This is not as simple as it sounds, because some varieties of string theory involve a universe with as many as ten dimensions.

Other theories include quantum gravity, which requires gravity to possess its own messenger boson (the graviton) in an attempt to make it more like the other forces. Then there is super-symmetry, which declares that there is a perfect symmetry hidden deep within the laws of nature—a symmetry which existed immediately after the Big Bang but has since then been lost in an asymmetric universe. Under supersymmetric theories, not only do all the known forces merge together into one, but the number of known particles doubles, for every particle must have a supersymmetric partner! It is the hope of many physicists that, like the Higgs boson, some of these supersymmetric particles might be within our grasp in the newest particle accelerators.

Index
••••••••

Glossary

············

Terms are explained where they
are introduced within the text;
however, a few are noted here for
the sake of clarity.

Antimatter a theory stating that
for every material particle in the
standard model there exists a
complementary particle with certain
opposite properties, such as electric
charge and spin.

Atom the fundamental unit of all
tangible matter, consisting of a nucleus
containing a mixture of protons and
neutrons and surrounded by
orbiting electrons.

Black hole any object so dense that
its gravitational attraction allows neither
matter nor electromagnetic radiation
to escape.

Electromagnetism the field of
physics concerning the behaviors
of electric and magnetic waves.

Energy a measurement of an object or
system's ability to do work. The motion,
or change in motion, of an object is
measured in terms of energy.

Force according to Newton's laws, that
which causes a change in an object's
motion. In the standard model, the four
fundamental forces are: strong force,
electromagnetic force, weak force,
and gravitational force.

Gravity the fundamental force that is
emanated from all matter and allows the
accumulation of celestial bodies.

Matter a collection of the fundamental
particles of physics. The opposite of
matter is either pure electromagnetic
radiation or a perfect vacuum.

Particle Accelerator a device
that employs powerful magnets to
accelerate fundamental particles and
force them to collide, resulting in the
production of secondary particles.

Quantum Physics a system
developed in the twentieth century
based on the notion that matter is best
described using rules of probability
and statistics rather than exact
measurements.

Radioactivity the phenomenon
in which an unstable atomic nucleus
decays, emitting either alpha, beta,
or gamma particles.

Relativity divided into Albert
Einstein's "special" and "general"
theories, the former is a four-
dimensional model redefining the
physical notions of both space and
time and the latter a refined theory
of gravitation.

Scientific method the logical systems
by which scientific hypotheses and
theories are developed.

Standard model the latest atomic
model that incorporates the most tested
physical theories and consists of four
fundamental forces and 16 fundamental
particles.

Thermodynamics a series of laws
by which properties of heat and
energy are defined.